AROMA SCIENCE

The Chemistry and Bioactivity
of Essential (

by Dr Maria Lis-E

BSc PhD

Published by Amberwood Publishing Ltd
Guildford, England.

© Amberwood Publishing Ltd 1995

First Edition June 1995
First Reprint April 1999

ISBN 1-899308-10-5

Cover design by Howland Northover

Printed in Great Britain

CONTENTS

Page No

1. INTRODUCTION 7
   Essential Oils and Aromatherapy

2. METHODS OF EXTRACTING ESSENTIAL OILS ... 9
   Extraction Techniques
   Chromatography
   Rectification and Adulteration

3. ESSENTIAL OIL COMPOSITION AND ANALYSIS 12
   Composition and Analysis Techniques
   Gas Chromatography

4. CHEMOTYPES AND OTHER VARIATIONS IN
   ESSENTIAL OILS 15
   Chemotypes
   Variation in Species and other differences
   International Standards
   Bioactivity
   General Toxicity
   Sensitisation, Irritation and Phototoxicity

5. OLFACTION – THE SENSE OF SMELL 20
   Physiology of Olfaction
   Functions and significance of Odours
   Consideration of the curative effect of Essential Oils
   Pharmacological action of Essential Oils
   Anti-stress action of Essential Oils
   Miscellaneous action of Essential Oils

6. ESSENTIAL OIL COMPOSITION 25
   Individual Components
   Illustrations

7. COMPENDIUM OF ESSENTIAL OILS WITH
   SCIENTIFIC DATA 28

8. BIBLIOGRAPHY 106

About the Author

Dr. Lis-Balchin graduated from London University with a BSc Honours Degree in Biochemistry and Zoology. She later went on to obtain her PhD while at Westminster Hospital Medical School. After many years in Medical research ;investigating the biochemical aspects of Neuropsychiatric and Neurological diseases at MRC, Carshalton and The Atkinson Morley Hospital she began doctoral research as a Toxicologist into protein absorption from the gut at the British Industrial Biological Research Association. She later continued her studies as a biochemist at Westminster Hospital Medical School and developed a particular interest in Pelargoniums which she used to exhibit at the Royal Horticultural Shows. She went on to study their medicinal, agrochemical properties and Essential Oils together with those of numerous other plants, comparing their chemical composition and biological properties.

Dr. Lis-Balchin is currently a senior lecturer in Toxicology, Nutrition and Biochemistry at South Bank University where she has pioneered a new unit at Degree and Master's level in the science of Essential Oils and Aromatherapy.

In addition to her studies, Dr. Lis-Balchin is a regular contributor at international conferences in Europe, the United States, South Africa, Australia and China on Essential Oils and Medicinal Plants.

Note to Reader

1 | Introduction

ESSENTIAL OILS

The Science of Essential oils encompasses their origins, structure and biological activity. The name "Essential oils" is misleading as the oils are not essential to us at all! They are simply oils which are volatile at room temperature i.e. eventually disappear leaving no mark, unlike ordinary oils and fats. They also have a characteristic odour which can change as they volatilize; this is due to the different components which have different volatilities; some of the components are said to be "top notes"and disappear very quickly while others are "bottom notes" and last longer. The same terms are used in perfumery, and this difference in volatility is one of the bases for blending in perfumery.

Essential oils are found in many different parts of plants e.g. petals, leaves, roots, fruit, bark etc. Due to these differences in distribution, different methods have to be used for extraction of the oils based mainly on the hardness of the organelle e.g. citrus fruit rinds can simply be squeezed to extract all the oil, whilst cinnamon bark has to be crushed and steam distilled.

Different plants will be grown in different parts of the world mainly for climatic reasons but also for economic reasons e.g. jasmine is no longer grown in the South of France as the cost of picking the flowers by hand is excessive compared to that in Egypt, where jasmine now flourishes. Different areas often demand different varieties of plant and this produces differences in the resultant essential oil e.g. Bourbon Geranium differs from Egyptian Geranium.

The biological activity of essential oils encompasses many clinical as well as pharmacological and agrochemical fields. This book deals only with those biological activities which have been scientifically determined and published in refereed journals or presented at International Conferences after acceptance by distinguished scientific committees. Anecdotal, clinical and biological activities are therefore omitted.

AROMATHERAPY

Aromatherapy is defined as: "treatment using scents or odours". This does not include massage per se. Essential oils are odorous, therefore can be used as the scent under this definition, but other scents cannot be excluded e.g. synthetic scented compounds.

Aromatherapy using essential oils can be applied by many methods:
a) a diffuser, usually powered by electricity, giving out a fine mist of the essential oil;
b) a burner, with water added to the fragrance to prevent burning;
c) ceramic or metal rings placed on electric light bulbs with a drop of essential oil;
d) a warm bath with drops of essential oil added;
e) a bowl with hot water and drops of essential oil;
f) compresses applied to the body dipped in water, hot or cold plus drops of essential oil;
g) massage of body using essential oils diluted in fixed oils e.g. almond, olive, wheatgerm, Aloe vera, coconut or sesame oils etc.

All these methods involve the *volatilization* of the essential oil and *inhalation* usually via the nose; this ensures that the fragrant molecules can activate the scent organs and exert their effect via the *Limbic System*. The essential oils can have a local effect on the nasal mucosa e.g. Camphor and Eucalyptus, used to clear blocked noses, cause a local irritation. Absorption via the nasal mucosa into the blood can also occur. Absorption via the lungs can occur easily as there is only one layer of cells between the alveoli and the blood capillaries. Massaging with essential oils (g) involves some absorption through the skin, but the actual amount absorbed is likely to be low due to the many layers of cells in the skin. Absorption from the bath is most unlikely as the oils not being miscible with water, float on the surface and volatilize quickly. They are, therefore, unlikely to come into contact with much of the body unless in extremely high concentrations. Mixing the essential oils with egg-yolk, cream or milk is not likely to improve the situation as an emulsion will be formed at best and the oils will volatilize more rapidly than be absorbed.

Note: Aromatherapy, as defined above, does NOT include ORAL intake. If essential oils are given by mouth, this becomes MEDICAL treatment and must be done under the supervision of a medically-qualified doctor NOT an Aromatherapist, however qualified the person may be.

2 | Methods of extraction of essential oils

Enfleurage

For very delicate petals e.g. rose. Layers of fat are separated by layers of rose petals, the essential oils passing from the rose to the fat. Eventually the essentials oils have to be extracted from the fat by solvents e.g. hexane. The hexane is then removed from the extract by a process of rectification and the oils are usually redissolved in alcohol to give an Absolute.

Solvent extraction

This is similar to the second and subsequent step of enfleurage whereby the plant material is extracted by solvents. The first stage produces a concrete which is then rectified and dissolved in alcohol to give the *Absolute*. The concrete contains most of the plant essential oils unchanged, The Absolute contains only the alcohol-soluble components.

Steam distillation

This method is the commonest extraction technique for essential oils. Steam or steam and water can be used. The plant material is extracted with water vapour at a high temperature in a still. The essential oils are then separated from the water after condensation; some essential oils remain in the water giving rise to Rose water etc. Some essential oil components undergo chemical transformations due to the drastic heat treatment and the resultant essential oil is often very different to that of the original in the plant e.g. German Chamomile oil contains a blue component called chamazulene *only* after distillation.

CO_2 extraction

Extraction with carbon dioxide is now very popular especially in the food industry as very pure essential oils are obtained and no solvents are left (CO_2 can be expelled easily just as we lose it in breathing out). The CO_2 extracted essential oils resemble those of solvent extraction and differ from the steam distilled oils. Most perfumers still prefer the latter.

Expression

Expression is used only for citrus oils. It involves squeezing the outer layers of the peel using manual means whereby the expressed oil is soaked into a sponge which is then itself squeezed out, or more commonly expression is carried out using mechanical means. Cold expression is used for lemon, orange, grapefruit, mandarin etc.

Rectification and Adulteration

The term rectification encompasses a large number of changes which can be made to an oil e.g. some components of the oil can be removed in order to make the oil more soluble in alcohol and longer lasting e.g. deterpenation involves removal of terpenes (all 'head' fractions). Deterpenation is used frequently for citrus oils.

Rectification can also cover certain adulterations. Many pure essential oils e.g. Melissa, or real "organic" oils are very rarely sold as they are very expensive.

Vacuum distillation - is used for most rectification and this involves fractional distillation under reduced pressure at a certain temperature (depending on what is to be removed).

Rectification primarily removes residual water and very light fractions from the 'heads', and heavy sesquiterpenes and waxes of high boiling point from the 'tails' of oils. Citrus oils are often de-sesquiterpenized.

Rectification can make different essential oils very similar (19).

Differential solubility – is also used for separating the more valuable oxygenated components from terpenes, as used for citrus oils industrially. The method involves cold temperatures and is based on the varying solubility of the fractions in a particular solvent e.g. aqueous alcohol. Centrifuges and counter-current extractors are also used.

Chromatography – using columns filled with silica gel etc. to separate off terpenes or other components.

Cutting

This is a means of making the original essential oil go further using a number of alternatives :

Nature-identicals – are composed of components obtained from plant sources, which could be from the same species or a completely different plant.

Synthetics – are composed of entirely synthetic components ie. chemicals made in the laboratory from various starting materials including plant components. Some are very cheap and nasty, whilst others are so similar to the natural product that most people cannot distinguish between them. Most expensive perfumes contain between approx. 50-100 ingredients, of which a high percentage are synthetics.

Substitutions – are often done using cheaper plant essential oils e.g. Petitgrain for Neroli or Ajowan for Thyme.

Dilutions - can be done using many chemicals and plant components to make a larger profit for the supplier e.g. DPG (dipropyl glycol), turpentine fractions, fixed oils.

Folding - involves mixing batches of the same essential oil, which can be stored for about 2 years and could then be processed further to terpeneless or sesquiterpeneless stages if required.

3 | Essential oil composition

Composition

Each essential oil is composed of 100-300 components, each of which has its own odour and physical/chemical characteristics. Most of the components called terpenoids are very similar and all arise from Acetyl (CH3 CO) units via either a 5-carbon unit called isoprene or via the shikimic pathway from amino acids. The terpenoids have either a 10-carbon structure – known as monoterpenoids or 15C i.e. sesquiterpenoids. Each of these can be oxygenated giving rise to a number of derivatives e.g. alcohols, aldehydes, phenols etc. Many of these components are very active due to their innate chemical structure and these components are often responsible for bioactivity e.g. cinnamaldehyde in cinnamon is a very potent bactericide as is eugenol in cloves and thymol in thyme.

Analysis

The best separation techniques available are gas chromatography with the addition of detectors utilizing mass spectroscopy (MS), nuclear magnetic resonance (NMR) or ultra-violet (UV) spectroscopy etc. The use of specialized capillary columns with numerous stationary phases allows for the separation and quantitization of most components in essential oils. However only very specialized techniques using cyclodextrins can show adulteration by synthetics. These involve the detection of stereoisomers which often differ in proportion in natural and synthetic essential oils. For example, Lavender adulterated with synthetic linalool or linalyl acetate has high racemic mixtures, whereas the pure Lavender has a different composition of enantiomers.

Gas chromatography

This simply involves a long column packed with an absorbent or coated with a non-volatile liquid. The essential oil, which is vaporized at the entry point, passes through the column with the help of the carrier gas, which is usually helium or hydrogen. The column is located in an oven in order to enable a change in temperature to be established e.g. from

70°C to 250°C at a given rate e.g. 3°C per minute, depending on the separation required and the particular essential oil.

The mixture of different chemical components will pass through the column at different speeds depending on their individual solubility between the stationary phase and the carrier gas. The least soluble components (in the stationary phase) pass through faster i.e. have a low Retention Time. The components are detected as they pass out of the column and appear on the chromatogram as a series of peaks.

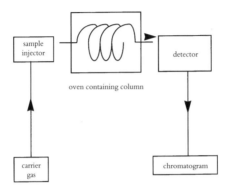

Diagram of GC apparatus

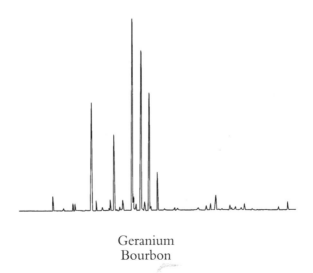

Geranium
Bourbon

This represents the fingerprint of an essential oil. Each peak represents one component - provided the conditions have been perfected. Each peak has an area which is dependent on its height and this is multiplied by ½ base i.e. the area of a triangle.

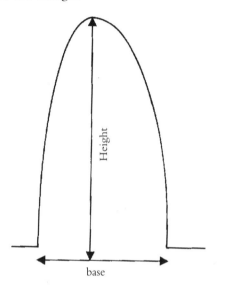

All peak areas are then added up to a total and then each individual peak area is calculated as a % of this total. This gives the basis for comparison with standard published data e.g. ISO.

| e.g. Lavender: | linalyl acetate | 30% |
| (Lavandula augustifolia) | linalool | 25% |

Usually the main peaks are compared, but sometimes minor peaks are especially important in showing adulteration.

e.g. Rose oil contains	approx. 0.59% cis Rose oxide
Rose damascena	and 0.2% trans Rose oxide
(Turkish)	

This, together with the other 200 components make up pure Rose oil. Cheap Rose oil can be made by using synthetic citronellol 30%, geraniol 25%, nerol 10% and phenylethylalcohol 3% + linalool 1%. The synthetic Rose oil costs about one thousandth that of pure Rose oil!

4 | Chemotypes and other variations in essential oils

Chemotypes

Some species have a tendency to produce variable seedlings e.g. thyme (Thymus vulgaris). This results in chemical variation in the oils produced by different plants giving rise to the term 'Chemotypes'. Different chemotypes can grow specifically in different areas, or else they can have a narrow distribution in one field. Plants raised by micropropagation often display great variability, and the only way to prevent changes in plants is by taking cuttings.

Species differences

There are many "groups" of essential oils which contain a number of different species under the same name. Examples are:

Chamomile

There are 3 main commercial Chamomile oils which originate from 3 different species of the same family, Compositae

German   –   Matricaria chamomilla
English   –   Anthemis nobilis
Moroccan   –   Ormenis mixta

Each of these oils has a different smell which is derived from the different chemical components (see page 37 and chromatograms on page 39). The use of one instead of another is therefore rather unscientific!

Eucalyptus

There are over 200 oil-producing Eucalyptus trees. The three main commercial Eucalyptus oils are:

E. globulus
E. citriodora
E. radiata

The odour and chemical composition of these three are again different (see page 50 and chromatograms on page 53).

Other Variations

The essential oil composition can vary in the same plant due to physicochemical variations e.g. temperature, humidity, seasonal changes, water, fertility of the soil, hours of sunlight, fertilizers applied etc. There is also a change in composition during the development of the leaves e.g. Geranium. There are also diurnal and nocturnal changes. The latter give the scientific basis for picking jasmine flowers early in the morning when the essential oils are at their best.

ISO

The International Organisation for Standardization of essential oils was largely set up for the Food and Cosmetics industries in order to establish criteria to ensure similarity of products.

However, as the composition of essential oils differs from season to season, batch to batch etc, 'blending' must often take place to ensure consistency in the product. 'Blending' may be done with different batches of the same essential oil, other essential oils or their components ie. 'nature identicals', or simply and most cheaply by the addition of synthetic components. The ISO may therefore unintentionally encourage adulteration.

Bioactivity

Scientific studies on bioactivity of Essential oils have largely been centred around *in vitro* tests. These are largely concerned with the anti-microbial and anti-fungal activity, with some pharmacological and biochemical evaluations. Prior to 1994, most of these tests were carried out on essential oil samples which were not fingerprinted using GC or GC/MS. Therefore, one can only assume the oils were pure and unadulterated. However, a survey carried out by the author (Lis-Balchin et al 1994) indicated that many commercial oils were very much adulterated and that there was an enormous variation in biological activity as well as chemical composition in the same 'named' oil. 16 Geranium oil samples showed a variation in activity ranging from 3-16 micro-organisms affected, and this was *not* related to the major components (31,34).

Toxicity

Toxicity is defined as an adverse effect caused by a compound. This can vary from feeling sick, vomiting, having a slight headache to a raging migraine; having tinnitus or suffering from vertigo; feeling aggressive to maniacal or homicidal; having a depression to feeling suicidal. It can cause dermatitis or the development of spots in a particular area or all over the body. The spots could be small and insignificant, or large exudating ones which are very itchy. Other symptoms can include feeling faint, having palpitations or blackouts; raised or lowered blood pressure etc. Most toxicity manifestations are however studied in animals like rats, who not only cannot express themselves about their feelings and tell us about headaches etc. but they also have a different physiology and metabolism e.g. they cannot vomit and cannot convert many compounds into the same metabolites as us. The only toxicity criteria measurable in the rat (or mouse) are: dermatitis (this is difficult unless the fur is shaven off!) also some Central Nervous System aberrations e.g. falling over, lying upside down etc.

LD50

The main toxicological evaluation is just concerned with the death of the animal ie. the LD50 is defined as the 'Lethal Dose which kills 50% of the animals'. It is therefore a number of grams (or mg or μg) which is related to the body weight of the animal e.g. g/Kg body weight. This dosage can then be extrapolated to man directly eg 10g/Kg is equivalent to 700g per 70Kg average man this is equivalent to eating 700g of sugar (which is considered non-toxic) in one sitting! Nobody could do this without vomiting and if pumped directly into the stomach, this dose of sugar would probably kill the person due to its hyperosmotic effect which would initially cause severe dehydration leading to collapse.

Any LD50 value over 5g/Kg is considered to be non-toxic; and values of 1-5g/Kg are relatively safe. The LD50 is however only a relative value of toxicity and it does not indicate long-term toxicity, teratogenicity or carcinogenicity.

Long-term effects can manifest themselves one to thirty years after a person has been subjected to small doses of chemicals. This is due to an accumulation of the chemical over a long period usually in a target organ or in the fat deposits around the body. Stress initiated by bereavement, divorce or losing weight can mobilise the chemical in large doses and cause toxic manifestations.

Teratogenic effects are seen only in the next generation, the mother or father having had no toxic symptoms after exposure to the chemical. The offspring, however, can be born deformed or limbless, or with defective internal organs which have not fully developed e.g. as the result of taking Thalidomide by expectant mothers during the first few months of pregnancy,

Carcinogenetic effects are often seen as part of long term usage of chemicals. It may be due to direct mutation of some cells or the production of a carcinogenic effect via a co-carcinogen etc.

Dermal and oral toxicity

There can be two effects of dermal application of chemicals (1) local skin effects e.g. reddening or dermatitis (2) Systemic effect in other parts of the body. The chemicals are absorbed almost directly into the blood stream and are therefore largely unchanged (unmetabolised). This is in contrast to an oral intake, where the chemical is 'digested' and therefore converted (metabolised) into many derivatives some of which may be more toxic than the original chemical. These new chemicals enter the blood stream and can attack target organs or tissues.

Because of the difference in the uptake of the chemical by the oral and dermal route, two LD50 values are given. The dermal LD50 is usually ascertained in the rabbit, which has a more sensitive skin compared to the rat.

Note of caution:

Although both the oral and dermal LD50 are quoted, the values for the essential oils described in this book are generally non-toxic. However, there is a possibility that the volatile oils could exert a toxic effect directly through intake into the respiratory tract. There is only one-cell thickness to traverse from the alveoli into the blood system. Therefore, like respiratory gases, the volatile lipophilic essential oils will be taken up very rapidly. There should therefore be some concern to both patient and aromatherapist but especially the latter, who is using essential oils all the time.

Absorption of essential oils through the respiratory tract can have a local or systemic effect (as in dermal absorption). The local effect could result in an asthmatic attack, breathlessness, wheezing or hyperventilation.

Sensitisation

This can be affected by the intake of the chemical via any route; oral, dermal or respiratory. Sensitisation involves the immune system. There may be a long period between the first impact of the chemical and a sensitisation reaction. The manifestation of the reaction is usually dermatitis or initially a local swelling e.g. almonds taken by sensitised people cause swelling of the larynx and this causes inability to breathe. The sensitisation reaction can be very violent e.g. anaphylactic shock, which causes a general collapse including breathing and blood pressure etc., and can be fatal within minutes.

Note of caution

Once a person is sensitised by a chemical even a distantly-related chemical to this can cause sensitisation. This is relevant to essential oils as many oils contain similar components. This aspect of toxicity has not been studied.

Irritation

In the case of dermal toxicity this refers to the effect on the skin. An irritation is an indication that the chemical has been absorbed and that the cells are reacting against it. The two main irritation manifestations are: reddening and swelling. This is usually studied using a 'patch test', whereby a constant amount of chemical is applied to a 1 inch square area of skin, which is then covered for 24hr, after which time the exposed area is evaluated for reddening and swelling. Note – the most sensitive parts of 'skin' in the body are those with soft or mucous membranes e.g. eyes, testes, vagina. Essential oils should not be applied here unless very diluted.

Phototoxicity

Refers to the effect of UV light on the chemical which may have already combined with a natural body compound. Sunlight or artificial UV light can have the same effect and it is unwise to use sunbeds after aromatherapy massage, especially if the blend had citrus oils in it. The phototoxic effect is similar to severe sunburn which can redden and burn the skin and cause desquamation. There could also be a tanning effect on the skin which may become blotched with brown pigmentation.

5 | Olfaction or the sense of smell

The sense of smell is one of the more primitive senses, belonging to the subjective world of feelings and emotions rather than the world of mind and intellect.

Smell or odour is sensed by two patches of nasal mucous membrane about 3-4cm^2 on the roof and upper part of the nasal cavity where ciliated nerve cells abound. The cilia actually protrude out of the mucosa and different odorant molecules (keys) fit exactly onto the different depressions on the cilia (locks or receptors). The nerve cell, which is now activated, conducts a signal to the brain via the Olfactory bulb to the Olfactory stalk and thence to the Thalamus and other parts of the Limbic System.

Complex mixtures of components as in essential oils, and even more so perfumes – which are composed of dozens of essential oils, must somehow register a pattern of activations and it is questionable whether pure components or synthetics would have a different effect on the mucosal cilia. There are very few people who can distinguish between pure and synthetic as long as the overall odour is what is expected. The ability to judge and even smell different odours is lost very rapidly if one smells perfumes or essential oils in quick succession – this can be easily demonstrated in the perfumery departments of large stores!

The smell can be recognised as nice or not by association with past experience. Pleasant experiences associated with a particular odour are more likely to make the odour nice and the odour itself can give a recall of the pleasant experience. Smell can be influenced by learning e.g. Perfumery Noses can detect incredibly subtle variations in odour of complex essential oils or perfumes. Smell can also be influenced by hormonal changes e.g. pregnancy can cause changes in the normal preference of odours as well as tastes e.g. often more sweet and milk-like odours been preferred. Many women at this time (as well as during menstruation or other parts of the Cycle) can become extremely sensitive to odours. Mothers can smell their own babies and even their excrement is pleasant to them. Babies can distinguish their mother by her individual odour and they can also respond to other odours almost at birth. Smell is influenced by culture e.g. the Japanese prefer more subtle aromas than the French.

Odours: their functions

Many animals can communicate by the use of biological odours. Activities like sexual behaviour, parent-offspring interactions, social recognition etc., can be influenced by odours. Even in the most developed human, smell is of great importance. Auxillary organs under the armpits are very pronounced and the odour emitted is greatly influenced by hormones in the endocrine system, including those resulting from stress. Amongst the odours emanating from the apocrine glands of males are androstenol (musky) and androstenone (urinary) which are synthesised in the testes and transported to the salivary glands via the general circulation. The same compounds are also largely produced by precursor breakdown by certain bacteria inhabiting the axillae. Thus some of the more pronounced bodily smells are of a sexual nature.

Odours can influence behaviour: some essential oils are relaxant whilst others are stimulating. Rovesti (49) reported that depressed patients could be treated with certain essential oils but this cannot be altogether totally successful judging by the vast number of depressed patients around. Personal idiosyncratic preference for odours can go against any generalisations. This can be well illustrated by looking at the immense perfumery industry which would be very much smaller if everybody liked one perfume! Perfumes are marketed specifically in order to arouse or enhance sexual attractiveness and make the wearer irresistible. Perfumes can however clash or synchronise with one's own body odour, perspiration and preference and therefore different perfumes suit different people.

Odours can influence the prospects of applicants during interviews (55, 56) in the same way as clothes, accent and body language.

Importance of odours to man

Historically, many scents have been associated with the god(s) due to the mind-bending and anaesthetising nature of their effect on man. 4000 years ago Egyptians burnt Kyphi – a mixture of precious odorants to appease the gods in the morning, at noon and at sunset – mainly in order to bribe the gods to let the Sun appear every day. Even before the Egyptians, the Chinese and Hindus were using incense for their gods. Even to this day, incense is used in churches and elsewhere; in fact it is almost universally used as it serves many purposes e.g. as a bloodless sacrifice, for casting out evil spirits or purification, mood setter for processions and festivities associated with Deities etc. (54). It is of profound interest that the choice of plants for incense is very narrow; only about 10 have been in common use over the centuries. These include:

Myrrh, Frankincense, Laudanum, Galbanum, Styrax, Cinnamon, Cassia and Sandalwood. It is even more interesting to find that some of the main odiferous components are structurally similar to androstenol and androstenone e.g. amyrin from myrrh! Thus sexual attractants are used to honour and appease the gods.

Many primitive tribes still use the smell of illness for diagnosis and scented plants for treatments. Different illnesses have specific smells, some of which are apparent to everybody e.g. Diabetes mellitus if uncontrolled gives the patient a smell of acetone from the breath. Other diseases have probably a more subtle smell, which can only be detected by a few – research into this field is under way. There is a historical but uncanny smell of death, which is impossible to describe but can instantly be recognised.

Odours can manipulate human behaviour in various ways. It is quite well known that the smell of freshly-baked bread provokes customers to buy more of everything in Supermarkets – not just bread.

Many frightening smells can be disguised using essential oils to the benefit of the patient e.g. hospital smells in general (reminiscent of cooked cabbage and urine) can have a stressful effect on patients especially before and after operations. The smell of rubber permeated with anaesthetic can also linger and any pleasant odour can over-rule the stress created and make recovery better. Use of essential oils during delivery have proved beneficial although the hormonal changes occurring can cause sickness in response to a well-liked odour.

The use of odorants in the workplace can also stimulate better production and growing numbers of offices and factories in Japan are employing essential oils like orange or rose or others alternatively during the day to good effect.

Can Essential oils cure illnesses?

Yes, but only certain illnesses, sometimes.

Essential oils cannot cure cancer or any other serious illness. They are not medicines or miracle cures. Their curative power resides in four basic functions:

Antimicrobial action
Pharmacological action
Anti-stress action
Miscellaneous action

Antimicrobial action – this has been shown for a large number of essential oils and this power has been used in the past to protect from plague, tend wounds and such-like. Applied locally and undiluted, many essential oils like Tea Tree can be effective, but there is no scientific proof that a drop or two of essential oil diluted in 10ml of carrier oil and massaged into the whole body can be effective against bacterial or fungal infestations in internal organs or tissues. The rapid rate of evaporation during massage of the volatile oils and incomplete absorption of the residual amount suggests that it could only act in a homeopathic way. Certainly, the assertion that essential oils kill only the bad organisms and leave the good ones is totally falacious as there is virtually no specificity of action exhibited by essential oils although different oils can affect different numbers of studied microorganisms (15, 33, 34).

Pharmacological action

Many essential oils like Geranium cause relaxation of smooth muscle and there is therefore scientific proof for the presumed activity of certain essential oils on the gut. However, again there is scant evidence to indicate that massaging with essential oils at low concentration can have an effect on internal organs. There is proof for the oral intake of undiluted essential oils (Pharmacopoeias) and many French doctors practising Aromatherapy have had good results using massive doses e.g. 15 ml per day given orally or rectally rather than the usual 0.1 to 0.3ml diluted in massage oil. However, dilutions of 1: 200,000 used on the ileum has shown potent activity *in vitro* (Lis-Balchin) therefore again action at great dilutions *in vivo* cannot be ruled out.

Anti-stress action

This is perhaps the most active mode of action of essential oils and the effect is probably through the Limbic System or other parts of the brain. Essential oils have often an effect on the CNV (Dodds) and on ability to perform tasks (Buchbauer) indicating that some are relaxant whilst others are stimulating. Massage is a known relaxant and this used in conjunction with relaxant essential oils can be seen to have an anti-stress effect.

Stress acts like shock or fright through hormonal (adrenaline effect) and secondary messengers and enzymes on body energy stores and intermediate metabolism. The net effect of a stress reaction is that known as the Fright/Fight response which causes an increase in heart rate and circulation rate together with other physiological effects which put the body on standby for immediate action. Once the stimulus disappears, all processes in the body return to normal. However under constant stress conditions, the body is under constant alert conditions and various symptoms appear including panic attacks, withdrawal symptoms, depression and various complications resulting from the physiological changes like high blood pressure, asthma, psoriasis, palpitations, nervous tension/exhaustion, mental breakdown, lowering of resistance to infection etc. In fact most diseases can be precipitated by stress.

Curing stress thereby could cure some associated illnesses. However, the use of essential oils alone cannot succeed, and has to be accompanied by changes in lifestyle, diet or other factors.

Miscellaneous action

Some essential oils have specific functions e.g. Lavender heals wounds. There is no scientific evidence on the mechanism of action, but since Gattefosse (19) first showed its curative effects there have been endless examples of its action. It may be that it acts through vitamin C which is essential to the repair of wounds (personal suggestion).

Gattefosse recommended the use of deterpenated essential oils i.e. non-pure adulterated oils which is far from the Holistic cry today. He further explained that many deterpenated oils became rather similar e.g. Lavender became similar to Bergamot. In fact Gattefosse was adamant that many experiments using essential oils failed to work if whole or pure oils were used.

Some oils e.g. Eucalyptus globulus and Camphor have a distinctive effect on the respiratory system by causing a local reaction on the mucosa which helps to clear the pathways. This effect is best shown through inhalation, as in using Vick's nasal spray or inhaling through gentle massage of the chest. The local action of essential oils like Camphor can again be beneficial through rubbing on the skin to relieve rheumatic or arthritic or other inflammatory conditions.

6 | Essential oil components

The hundreds of components of essential oils are nearly all derived from the common unit of energy of intermediate metabolism called *Acetyl Coenzyme A*, which when non-activated is simply acetic acid (or vinegar!). There are many stages in the synthesis of essential oil components, but the main common denominator is the production of *isoprene* units. These are 5-carbon compounds:

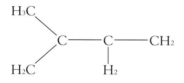

When two of these units join, 10-carbon compounds (C10) are formed. These are called:

Monoterpenes, e.g. α-pinene and β-pinene of Pine needle oil, limonene of Citrus oils, g-terpinene of Marjoram and p-cymene of Frankinsence.

The Monoterpenes can become oxidised to give large numbers of:

Alcohols (–OH) e.g. citronellol and geraniol of Geranium and Rose oils, linalool of Lavender, Petitgrain and Rosewood, menthol of Peppermint, lavandulol of Lavandin and borneol of Yarrow.

Ketones (C=O) are often chemically reactive and relatively toxic, but not invariably. Examples of ketone components include pulegone of Pennyroyal oil, thujone of Dalmatian Sage, menthone and isomenthone of Peppermint and Geranium oil, camphor of Camphor oil and carvone of Caraway oil. Trace amounts of β-damascenone, β-damascone and β-ionone are largely responsible for imparting the characteristic fragrance of Rose oil.

Aldehydes (–CHO) are also often chemically reactive compounds and include citronellal of Citronella, citral of Lemongrass, α-santalene of Sandalwood, anisaldehyde of Star Anise and Perillaldehyde of Perilla.

Esters (acetates, formates etc.) e.g. Geranyl tiglate and citronellyl formate of Geranium oil, linalyl acetate of Lavender and Bergamot, geranyl acetate of Ho Wood and Palmarosa.

Oxides e.g. Rose oxide of Geranium and Rose oils; 1,8-cineole of Eucalyptus radiata, Cajuput, Tea-tree and Rosemary.

Phenylpropanes are another group of components and are derived from the amino acid *phenylalanine*. These include estragol of Basil, saffrole of Sassifras, anethole of Anise oil and Fennel oil. Phenols including thymol of Thyme, Eugenol (and isoeugenol) of Clove oil and carvacrol of Oregano and Savory are very active as is cinnamaldehyde of Cinnamon oil.

Other important essential oil components include: Coumarins and furocoumarins, the latter in Bergamot and citrus oils, myristicine of Nutmeg and acetyl salicylic acid of Wintergreen oil.

There are also numerous aliphatic hydrocarbons, aldehydes, ketones etc. which occur as essential oil components e.g. 2-decanone, 2-undecanone, 2-undecanol, 2-undecyl-2-methylbutyrate in Rue oil.

Sesquiterpenoids

When three isoprene units join up, sesquiterpenoids of 15 carbon units are formed. These can be terpenes e.g. chamazulene of German Chamomile oil, or oxidation products as before eg. α-santalol of Sandalwood oil, β-caryophyllene of Clove oil, β-elemene of Amyris oil, β-eudesmol of Eucalyptus radiata, patchouline from Patchouli oil and guaia-6, 9-diene of Geranium oil.

Other important compounds from isoprene units

Four isoprene units joined together give rise to *Diterpenoids* (C20) e.g. gibberellic acid (a plant hormone). Six units give *Triterpenoids* (C30) e.g. phytosterols and saponins. Eight units give *Carotenoids* (C40), which also give rise to *Vitamin A* as well as the other fat-soluble *vitamins D, E* and *K*, and also cholesterol and the sex hormones. When more than several hundred isoprene units join up to give C1000 or more, natural rubber is produced.

Most of these products can only be produced in plants, except for the steroids. It is interesting to note that many essential oil components bear some resemblance to steroid hormones e.g. sclareol, giving rise to speculation regarding medicinal properties.

Properties of components

It is wrong to group essential oil components of similar chemistry e.g. ketones, aldehydes etc. together and allocate biological properties to these groups. With few exceptions, similar components can influence the action of different essential oils in different ways. In an extensive study of biological activities of different essential oils, no correlation was found with the main components, except in the case of spasmogenic action on smooth muscle correlating with monoterpenes. However, *not all* monoterpenes had the same effect (Lis–Balchin et al. 1994).

COMPONENT FORMULAE

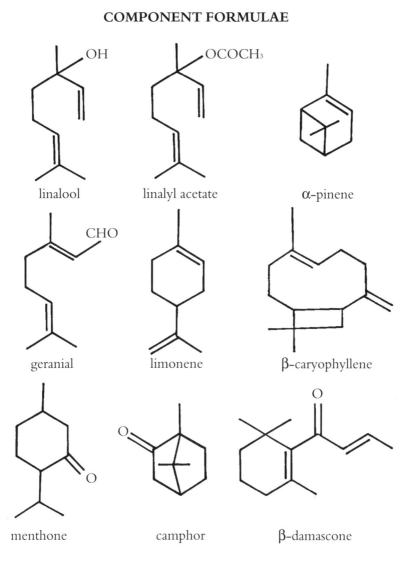

linalool

linalyl acetate

α-pinene

geranial

limonene

β-caryophyllene

menthone

camphor

β-damascone

7 | Compendium of essential oils with scientific data

BASIL~   *Labiatiae*
Ocimum basilicum L.
Sweet Basil oil – Linalool type
Exotic – Camphor-Estragole type
Methyl-cinnamate type
Plus many more chemotypes

Extraction: Steam distillation of flowering tops of plants
Origin: Egypt, France, USA, Italy.

Main components, %

	Sweet	*Exotic*	*Met-Cinnamate*
1,8-cineole	3-27	3-7	5.6
Methyl-chavicol	0-30	68-87	2.2
Methyl eugenol	0-7	0.5-2.4	0
Eugenol	0-7	trace	0
Z-methyl cinnamate	0	0	4.7
E-methyl cinnamate	0	0	32
Linalool	44-69	0.3-2.2	41.7
β-caryophyllene	0.7-14.4	0	0

There is an enormous variation in the components within and between the different groups.

Sweet Basil has GRAS status.

Adulteration
Many different types of Basil oil are available and many are "doctored" by the addition of synthetic Linalool to the so-called Exotic Basil oils.

Toxicity
LD_{50} – Sweet oil; 1.4g (<3.5)/kg (oral) rat; 0.5g/kg (dermal) rabbit.
Irritation/Sensitisation – Nil at 4% (Human).
Phototoxicity – Nil reported.

Note: Methyl chavicol is a suspected sensitiser, therefore the more exotic type oils may cause sensitisation reactions in some people.
Other chemotypes e.g. methyl-cinnamate types from Fiji etc. have not been tested.

Bioactivity

Pharmacology – There was an initial spasmogenic action followed by a spasmolytic action on guinea-pig ileum *in vitro* (32).
Antibacterial action – Was good; 15/25 different bacteria were affected by an unspecified basil (32) and 15/25 were affected by a methyl-chavicol-high basil together with 20/20 Listeria monocytogenes varieties (32), while another study showed that basil oil had an effect on 5/5 Listeria by limiting the growth (6). Sweet Basil oil vapour had an effect against 1/5 bacteria (42).
Antifungal action – Sweet Basil was moderately to very active against 5/5 fungi (38). Methyl-chavicol-rich basil was very active against 3/3 fungi (32). Sweet Basil oil had a good action against 13/15 fungi (41)
Miscellaneous action – Basil is a stimulating oil according to CNV data (36). Basil had no antioxidant activity (32).

BERGAMOT~   *Rutaceae*
Citrus bergamia Risso
syn.C.aurantium L.subsp.bergamia Wright & Arn.

Extraction Expressed oil from orange rind. Can be rectified.
Origin: Italy

Main components, %

Linalyl acetate	23-35
Limonene	19-38
Linalool	4-29
α-terpinene	4-13
β-pinene	3-13

Special minor components
Furocoumarin content approx. 0.44% is responsible for phototoxicity (see below). FCF = Furocoumarin-free oils are specially rectified and these are non-phototoxic.
Trace components contributing greatly to the odour include (–) – guaienol, (+) – spathulenol, nerolidol, farnesol and β-sinensal (45)
Bergamot oil has GRAS status.

Adulteration

Synthetic linalyl acetate with/without linalool is often used as a cheap additive or substitute. Limonene is also added sometimes. Other adulterants include: Bitter Orange Oil, Lime oil, synthetic or natural citral, terpinyl acetate or diethyl phthalate etc.

Toxicity

LD_{50} – >10g/kg (oral) rat; >20g/kg (dermal) rabbit.
Irritation/Sensitisation – Nil at 30% (human). 3/200 patients with dermatitis affected (50).
Phototoxicity – Exposure to sunlight or UV light eg. sunbeds following skin application of Bergamot and other expressed citrus oils causes pigmentation of the skin (berloque dermatitis) and/or burning. This is caused by the furocoumarins or bergaptens in the oil and the degree of phototoxicity is directly related to the percentage of these chemicals in the oil. There is a natural progression of severity from Bergamot > Lime > Bitter Orange > Lemon > Grapefruit > Sweet Orange > Tangerine > Mandarin > Tangelo. When the level of furocoumarins is decreased to below 0.0075%. phototoxicity is avoided (26). Therefore from sweet orange onwards there is virtually no danger of phototoxicity. However

this does not take into account the idiosyncracies of different individuals. *It is recommended that FCF oils are used and that sunbeds are avoided after any exposure to citrus oils.*

Bioactivity

Pharmacology – It is a mainly spasmolytic oil with some initial spasmogenesis as shown on guinea-pig ileum *in vitro* (32). However the oils tested proved to be adulterated.

Antibacterial action – Was shown against 11/25 bacteria (15) and 19-22/25 bacteria and 11-19/20 Listeria monocytogenes varieties (32) 1/5 bacteria were affected by the vapour (42)

Antifungal action – One of two samples of oil showed moderate activity against 5 different fungi (38) and poor to moderate activity against 3 fungi (32). Poor action was found against 15 fungi, whilst the terpeneless oil showed an even lower action (41)

Miscellaneous action: CNV studies indicated that Bergamot had a sedative action in man (36,57). One of two samples showed moderate antioxidant action (32).

CAJEPUT~ *Myrtaceae*

syn.Cajuput, Punk tree
Melaleuca leucadendron L.
syn.M.cajeputi, M.quinquenervia (S.T.Blake)

Extraction Distilled twigs and fresh leaves of tree.
Origin: India,Indonesia

Main components, %

1,8-cineole	14-69
α-pinene	8.0
β-pinene	1.1
Limonene	trace
Linalool	3.5

Cajuput has GRAS status.

Adulteration

Cajeput can be replaced by cheaper Eucalyptus oil e.g. E.globulus or a combination of Eucalyptus (Pharmaceutical) with traces of terpinyl acetate, terpinyl propionate and terpineol esters. Niaouli is very similar to Cajeput but costs about the same.

Toxicity

LD_{50} - 4g/kg (oral) rat; >5g/kg (dermal) rabbit.
Irritation/Sensitisation - Nil at 4% (human).
Phototoxicity - Nil.

Bioactivity

Pharmacology - A weak spasmolytic activity with an initial spasmogenic activity was found against guinea-pig ileum *in vitro* (32).
Antibacterial action - Against 21/25 bacterial species and 19/20 Listeria monocytogenes varieties (32). Cajuput had activity against 3/5 bacteria (40) and the vapour against 1/5 bacteria (42).
Antifungal action - Against 5 fungi (38)and virtually nil activity against 3 fungi (32). Low activity was reported against 15 fungi (41).
Miscellaneous action - No antioxidant activity was found (32).

Uses

Cajuput is used as a carminative (internally) the dose is 0.05-0.2ml. It is used as a mild rubefacient (externally) and is included in a number of ointments and liniments (37).

CAMPHOR~ *Lauraceae*
Cinnamomum camphora (L.) Nees & Ebermeier
syn. C.camphora Sieb.

Extraction Steam distilled trees in Japan (hon-sho), Formosa (Hon-sho, Yu-sho), China (Yu-sho)
Origin:China

The crude oil has crystalline camphor, which is removed by filterpressing. The oil is then vacuum-rectified giving extra camphor plus three fractions :
1. White Camphor oil or light fraction or 860-880 oil
2. a) Brown Camphor oil or medium-heavy or 1070 oil, containing a minimum of 80% safrole; sassafras odour distinctive.
b) Yellow Camphor oil or residual oil after removing safrole from brown oil or 960-980 oil; sassafras odour.
3. Blue Camphor oil or the heaviest fraction, containing mainly sesquiterpenes: this fraction is rarely used.

Main components, %

	White Camphor %
1,8-cineole	30.2
α-pinene	6.8
Camphor	50.8
Terpineol	2.1
Sesquiterpenes	variable

Camphor White and Yellow have GRAS status.

Adulteration

Unlikely due to wide availability of the oils and low price. However, the composition of the oils can vary dramatically.

Toxicity

LD_{50}
White – >5ml/kg (oral)rat; >5ml/kg (dermal) rabbit.
Yellow – 4g/kg   >5g/kg.
Brown – 2.5ml/kg   >4ml/kg.
Irritation/Sensitisation – White – Nil at 20% (Human), Yellow – 4%, Brown – 4%.
Phototoxicity – Nil.

Bioactivity

Pharmacology – A strong spasmogenic activity was shown against guinea-pig ileum *in vitro* (32). There was an increase in tone and rhythmic contractions plus peristalsis in dog small intestine *in vivo* (47).

Antibacterial action – White camphor had a very strong action against 25/25 different bacteria and 16/20 Listeria monocytogenes varieties (32).

Antifungal activity – White camphor was active against 5 fungi whilst Sassafrassy camphor was less active (38); White camphor was very active against 3 fungi (32)

Miscellaneous action – The use of camphor in various nasal decongestants and muscular rubifacients is well known.

CEDARWOOD~ *Cupressaceae*
Pinaceae

Atlas Cedarwood – Cedrus Atlantica Manetti (Pinaceae)
Texas Cedarwood – Juniperus mexicana Spring. (Cupressaceae)
Virginian Cedarwood – Juniperus virginiana L. (Cupressaceae)

Extraction: Steam-distilled finely comminuted waste wood (also Cedarleaf oil produced from leaves and twigs of Thuja occidentali.
Origin: North Africa/USA/East Africa/China

Main components, %

	Range	*Atlas*	*Virginia*	*Texas*
Cedrol	1.4–31.6	16.5	24.0	26.8
α- Cedrene	15.8–30.9	6.5	3.1	4.5
β-Cedrene	1.4–7.7	24.6	21.3	31.5
Thujopsene	14.6–34.7	29.2	10.2	17.8

Examples of the composition of commercial oils labelled as Atlas, Virginia and Texas are given showing the similarity between them.

Only Virginian Cedarwood has been granted temporary usage in foods.

Adulteration

There is substantial adulteration and blending of the oils and there is no real demarcation between the commercial Cedarwood oils, although there is a botanical difference between the species and one of the Cedarwoods (Texas) is even in a different family.

Toxicity

LD_{50} –
Texas cedarwood; >5g/kg (oral) rat;   >5g/kg (dermal) rabbit.
Virginia cedarwood; >5g/kg (oral) rat; >5g/kg (dermal) rabbit.
Atlantic cedarwood; >5g/kg (oral) rat; >5g/kg (dermal) rabbit.
Irritation/Sensitisation – nil at 8% (human).
Phototoxicity – nil reported.

Bioactivity

Pharmacology – There was a small spasmolytic action on guinea-pig ileum *in vitro* (32) by Texas, Virginia and Atlas Cedarwood oils. Texas Cedarwood oil had a weak therapeutic effect on experimental tuberculosis of the guinea-pig when combined with subeffective doses of dihydrostreptomycin (18).
Antibacterial action – Was virtually absent in Texas, Virginia and Atlas

Cedarwoods: 3,4,5/25 bacteria were slightly affected respectively and there was no action on 25 different Listeria monocytogenes varieties by any of the Cedarwood oils (32); a Cedar oil had no activity against 5/5 bacteria studied (59). The vapour of Cedarwood Texas inhibited the growth of 2/5 bacteria (42). Cedarwood oil Texas had no effect on Tubercle bacilli (18).

Antifungal action – Was virtually zero on 3/3 fungi investigated using Texas,Virginia and Atlas Cedarwood oils (32) and 1/15 fungi (41).

Miscellaneous action – There was no antioxidant action apparent in either Texas, Virginia nor Atlas Cedarwood oils (32).

CHAMOMILES~ *Compositae*

GERMAN Chamomile – Matricaria recutica L.
syn. M.chamomilla L.
MOROCCAN Chamomile – Ormenis multicaulis (L.)
syn.O.mixta
ROMAN Chamomile – Chamaemelum nobile (L.) All
syn.Anthemis nobilis L.

Extraction: Steam-distilled flowers and tops.
Origin: Egypt/Morocco/England repectively

Main components, %

German		Moroccan		Roman	
German		*Moroccan*		*Roman*	
cis-spiro ether	1	α-pinene	15	methyl-angelate	16
chamazulene	1-18	santolina alc.	32	3-methylpentyl isobutyrate	12
α-bisabolol oxide B	11	transpinocarveol	3	2-methylbutyl angelate	4-25
α-bisabolol oxide A	9	germacrene	5		
α-bisabolol	10				
Farnesene	15-28				

The three Chamomiles each have a distinctive odour and entirely different composition and originate from different species of Compositae, Although, according to most Aromatherapy books there is virtually no difference in their activity and "Chamomile" alone is used! There is a difference in the price however, which often influences the buyer; the German oil is the most expensive and the Moroccan the least.The latter is therefore often favoured by people who have had no chemical and olfactory exposure to the three oils. A good indication of a German oil is its dark blue colour (due to chamazulene) which is absent from the other two...however, this is not always easy to see through brown bottles! German and Roman Chamomiles have GRAS status.

Adulteration

Synthetic chamazulene is often added to "improve" the quality of German Chamomile, as there is a direct correlation between colour and quality; ageing of the oil also leads to a deterioration in the colour to a pale green and even brown. Chamazulene could also be added to Moroccan Chamomile in order to fool the buyer that it was the more expensive German oil. Some producers extract flowers of Matricaria recutica with solvents which results in an ink-blue colour with a high viscosity; this can then be added to low-grade oils.

Toxicity

LD_{50} – >5g/kg (oral) rat; >5g/kg (dermal) rabbit for German & Roman.
Irritation & Sensitisation – nil at 4% for German & Roman (human).
Phototoxicity – Nil for German & Roman.
Note: No toxicity data is available for Moroccan Chamomile.

Bioactivity

Pharmacology – German Chamomile and its components α-bisabolol and bisabolol oxides A & B and cis-spiro ether had a spasmolytic action on guinea-pig ileum *in vitro* (1) the action of German Chamomile was confirmed on the same tissue (32) and Roman Chamomile showed a similar spasmolytic action, with one sample giving an initial spasmogenic action; Moroccan Chamomile showed a very slight spasmolytic action (32).

Antibacterial action – Chamomiles in general have a very weak antibacterial action a "Chamomile" was active against only 1/25 different bacteria (15); German Chamomile showed activity against 3, 6/25 bacteria; Roman against 3, 5/25 bacteria and Moroccan against 6, 17/25 bacteria (32). Against Listeria monocytogenes, German Chamomile was active very slightly against 1/5 Listeria varieties whilst Roman Chamomile was active slightly against 5/5 varieties (6). Other studies (32) showed that German Chamomile was active against 0 and 1/20; Roman against nil and Moroccan against 1 and 11/25 varieties.

Antifungal action – German Chamomile showed very low activity against 3 fungi; Roman Chamomile and Moroccan were similar (32).

Miscellaneous action – German Chamomile showed antioxidant action, Roman had no action and one of two Moroccan samples showed antioxidant action (32). "Chamomile" was found to be a sedative oil according to CNV results (36,57)

Uses

Chamomile Tea is a very soothing drink made from dried flower-heads and containing the essential oil (usually made from Roman Chamomile). German Chamomile has anti–inflammatory activity and is used in various medicinal concoctions in Europe e.g. as a poultice; Roman Chamomile is also used for the same purpose. Both herbs are used for rinsing blond hair and included in shampoos etc. (37).

Experiments on patients with ventricular catheterisation showed that in 12/12 patients Chamomile tea prepared from Matricaria had no significant cardiac effects. However a marked hypnotic effect was observed and 10 minutes after drinking the tea 10/12 patients fell asleep, the deep sleep lasting about 90 minutes. (37)

"Kamillosan", an extract of Chamomile 10% with the volatile oil at 0.5% (Roman) is used as an ointment for cracked nipples and nappy rash.

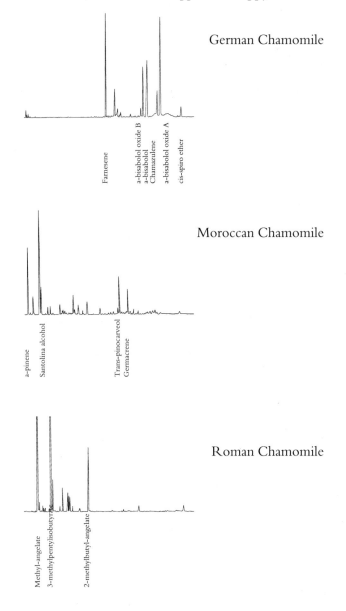

CINNAMON~   *Lauraceae*
Cinnamomum zeylanicum Nees.
syn. C.verum Presl.
syn.Laurus cinnamonum

Extraction: steam distilled bark or leaf of trees.
Origin: Sri-Lanka, India, Indonesia.

Main components, %

	Cinnamon bark	Leaf
α-pinene	0.2-0.6	0.2-1.0
p-cymene	0.6-1.2	0.4-1.2
Cinnamaldehyde	74-75	1.3-2.0
Eugenol	0.8	70-96
Cinnamyl acetate	5.0	0.8-1.7
Caryophyllene	1.4-3.3	1.9-5.8
Benzyl benzoate	0.7-1.0	2.7-3.5

Note: There is a profound difference in the composition of the two oils and they are not to be substituted; the bark contains mainly Cinnamaldehyde, whilst the leaf resembles Clove bud oil in containing mainly Eugenol.

Both Cinnamon bark and leaf have GRAS status.

Adulteration

Cinnamon bark oil is often cut with cinnamon leaf oil, Canella bark oil, Clove leaf oil, eugenol, cinnamic aldehyde etc. Cassia oil is often used as a substitute. Cinnamon leaf oil is often substituted by Clove leaf oil, Bay leaf oil and synthetic eugenol mixtures. Other crude diluents are used such as fuel oil, kerosene, petroleum etc.

Toxicity

LD_{50} –
Cinnamon leaf oil – 2.7g/kg (oral) rat; >5g/kg (dermal) rabbit.
Cinnamon bark oil – 3.4g/kg (oral) rat; 0.7g/kg (dermal) rabbit.
Irritation/Sensitisation – Cinnamon leaf oil: nil at 10%.
Cinnamon bark oil: nil irritation at 8% but sensitisation produced in 20/25 volunteers.
Note: Cases of acute contact sensitivity have been reported when Cinnamon bark oil was used in a dentifrice(18).
Phototoxicity – Nil reported.

Bioactivity

Pharmacology – Cinnamon leaf oil had a small spasmolytic action on guinea-pig ileum *in vitro* (32).

Antibacterial action – Is very potent e.g. an unspecified Cinnamon oil was very active against 5/5 bacteria(59), another unspecified Cinnamon was active against 23/25 different bacteria (15) and Cinnamon leaf oil was active against 24/25 bacteria and 20/20 Listeria monocytogenes varieties(32) and in another study 5/5 Listeria were greatly affected (6). The vapour had a strong effect against 5/5 bacteria (42).

Antifungal action – Cinnamon leaf oil was active against 3/3 fungi (32). Cinnamon was very active against 18/18 fungi including Trichophyton mentagrophytes (41).

Miscellaneous action – Cinnamon leaf showed a strong antioxidant action (32).

Uses

Cinnamon oils have been used for several years in dental medicine, and as a germicidal agent in toothpaste. They are also carminative and have been used in the treatment of diarrhoea (dose; 0.3-1.2ml of cinnamon spirit – ie. 10% oil in alcohol). The oils can also be used as an inhalant in boiling water (37).

There is a temporary acceptable daily intake of cinnamaldehyde of up to 700µg per kg body weight per day (37).

CITRONELLA~ *Graminae*

Cymbopogon nardus (Rendle)
Andropogon nardus L.
Andropogon nardus Ceylon de Jong

Extraction: Steam distillation of the dried grass.
Origin: Sri Lanka, Java, Formosa, Taiwan, Indonesia, India, China.

Main components, %

Geraniol	11-26
Citronellol	4-24
Citronellal	5-48
Limonene	3-9
Camphene	0-8
Sesquiterpenes	variable

Citronella oil has GRAS status.

Adulteration

Citronella oil is cheap and therefore adulteration by other oils is not very likely. Citronella itself is used for cutting Geranium oil and Rose oil.

Toxicity

LD_{50} – >5g/kg (oral) rat; 4.7 (3.4-6.7) g/kg (dermal) rabbit.
Irritation/Sensitisation – Nil at 8% (human). Applied neat to skin of rabbit it caused irritation. 5/22 patients with dermatitis were sensitive to Citronella oil (52).
Cases of eczematous, contact-type hypersensitivity to Citronella oil have been reported as has folliculitis of the acneform type, and papulovesicular eczema of hands, fingers and fore-arms. Oil of Citronella in perfumes has been listed as a primary irritant and sensitiser (18).
Phototoxicity – Not tested.

Bioactivity

Pharmacology – A spasmolytic effect was produced on guinea-pig ileum *in vitro* (32).
Antibacterial action – Citronella oil was active against 3/5 bacteria (59) and the vapour against 2/5 bacteria (42).
Antifungal action – Formosan Citronella was active against 5/5 fungi (38). Low activity, mainly fungistatic was found against 14/15 fungi (41).
Miscellaneous action – Nil reported

Uses

Used as an insect repellent either alone or in conjunction with other essential oils eg. Geranium, Palmarosa etc.

CLARY SAGE~   *Labiatiae*
Salvia sclarea L.

Extraction: Steam-distilled flowering tops and leaves.
Origin: Morocco, Russia
As Clary Sage differs dramatically from other Sages it is treated separately.

Main components, %
Linalyl acetate	63-74
Linalool	8-28
Caryophyllene	1-2
Sclareol	0.8-2
Germacrene D	0.4-4

Minor components: there are over 250 components and it is the trace ones which contribute to the odour e.g. dihydropyran, some cyclic ethers, γ-lactones, (+) – spathulenol, (+) – isospathulenol and sclareol.
Clary Sage has GRAS status.

Adulteration

Synthetic Linalyl acetate and Linalool may be added, or Lavender oil, Mentha citrata (Bergamot Mint) etc.

Toxicity

LD_{50} – 5g/kg (oral) rat; >2g/kg (dermal) rabbit.
Irritation/Sensitisation – Nil at 8% (human); 1/200 dermatitis patients affected (50).
Phototoxicity – Nil.

Bioactivity

Pharmacology – There was an initial spasmogenic action followed by a spasmolytic action on guinea-pig ileum *in vitro* (32).
Antibacterial action – Was shown against 11-18/25 different bacteria and 9-15/20 Listeria monocytogenes varieties (32). 1/5 bacteria were affected by the vapour (42).
Antifungal action – Was slight against 3/5 fungi (38) but moderate to good action against 3/3 fungi (32).
Miscellaneous action – No antioxidant effect was found (32).

Uses

Although often quoted as oestrogenic, no scientific data were found in support of this statement.

CLOVE~   *Myrtaceae*
Eugenia caryophyllata Thunb.
Clove bud oil
Clove leaf oil
Clove stem oil

Extraction: steam or water distillation of the buds, leaves or stems of the tree.
Origin: Madagascar, Zanzibar, Comoro

Main components, %

	Clove Bud	*Clove Leaf*	*Clove Stem*
Caryophyllene	2-12	15-19	2.5-3.5
Eugenol	36-95	77-90	87-95
Acetoeugenol	11-22	trace	trace
Humulene	0.5-1.6	1.5-2.5	0.3-0.4
Eugenyl acetate	6-12	0.5-10	2-5

All three Clove oils have GRAS status.

Adulteration
Due to the price differential, Clove bud oil is often adulterated; or substituted for by Clove leaf or stem oil. The price of synthetic eugenol and caryophyllene is higher than the natural oils.

Toxicity
LD_{50} –
Clove bud oil – 2.7-3.7g/kg (oral) rat; >5g/kg (dermal) rabbit.
Clove leaf oil – 1.4g/kg (oral) rat; 1.2g/kg (dermal) rabbit.
Clove stem oil – 2-3.7g/kg (oral) rat; >5g/kg (dermal) rabbit.
Irritation/Sensitisation – Clove bud oil – nil at 5% on human volunteers and no effect at 0.2% on patients with dermatoses. When tested at 20% in an ointment, 2/25 subjects showed primary irritation reactions (erythema).
Clove leaf oil – Nil at 5%.
Clove stem oil – Nil at 10%. No irritation produced on subjects at 2% and at 0.2% on dermatoses patients. When tested at 20% in an ointment, 2/25 subjects showed primary irritation reactions (erythema)
Phototoxicity – Nil reported.

Bioactivity
Pharmacology – Both Clove bud oil and Clove leaf oil produced a small spasmolytic action on the guinea-pig ileum *in-vitro* (32). In rat, guinea-

pig and rabbit organs, Clove oil, stem and bud, was found to have antihistamine and musculotropic spasmolytic activity and papaverine-like antispasmodic activity against isolated small intestine of the mouse (18).

Antibacterial action − Is very strong; 4/5 bacteria were affected by an unspecified Clove oil (59); 23/25 different bacteria were affected by another unspecified Clove oil. Clove bud oil and Clove leaf oil affected 23, 24/25 bacteria respectively and both affected 20/20 Listeria monocytogenes varieties (32) and in another study 5/5 Listeria were strongly affected (6). Studies in the past revealed that Clove oil was 8.5 times more active than phenol; rectified Clove oil showed less antibacterial action than the normal oil (18). Clove oil vapour affected 2/5 bacteria and the rectified oil vapour 1/5 (42).

Antifungal action − Was variable; four different Clove oils from bud, stem and leaf had poor to good effects on 5/5 fungi (38). Clove bud and Clove leaf oils both had an identical effect on 3/3 fungi (32). Clove oil was active against 15/15 fungi (41). Madagascan redistilled Clove leaf, rectified Clove stem and Zanzibar redistilled clove stem oils greatly inhibited 3/3 wood-destroying fungi (18). Clove oil had a strong effect against 18/18 fungi including Trichophyton mentagrophytes (41).

Miscellaneous action − Both Clove bud oil and Clove leaf oil had a strong antioxidant action (32).

Uses

Both Clove bud oil and Clove stem oil are used in dentistry as a local anaesthetic for toothache and for the treatment of dental cavities where it damages the dental pulp but does not irritate the dentine. Toothache drops − Odontalgicum consist of 25g of chlorbutol with Clove oil to 100ml; Clove oil mixed with zinc oxide forms a temporary filling (37). Clove stem and bud oil are used as a counterirritant and a carminative and are also included in patented formulations for food preservatives, air disinfectants, and cosmetic and medical uses; they are also patented for external use in the treatment of degeneration of bone, inflammation of joints, bursitis, and treatment of sinuses (18).

CUBEB~ *Piperaceae*
Piper cubeba L.

Extraction: Steam distillation of the mature, unripe, sun-dried fruit after crushing or course grinding.
Origin: Indonesia, Java, Borneo, Sumatra, African Congo.

Main components, %

Sabinene	4.6
α-cubebene	7.1
β-cubebene	11.0
Copaene	10.4
Caryophyllene	3.7
Alloaromadendrene	4.2
γ-humulene	4.9
δ-cadinene	8.8
Cubebol	10.0

The composition varies with source, but consists mainly of sesquiterpenes.

Cubeb oil has GRAS status.

Adulteration

Various oils of related species e.g. Piper crassipas Konthals and P. lowang Blume etc.

Toxicity

LD_{50} – 5g/kg (oral) rat; 5g/kg (dermal) rabbit.
Irritation/Sensitisation – Nil at 8% (human). However, applied undiluted to the skin of mice and swine it produced hyperkeratosis and dry desquamation and was irritating.
Phototoxicity – Nil.

Bioactivity

Pharmacology – A weak spasmolytic effect was produced on guinea-pig ileum *in vitro* (32).
Antibacterial action – Cubeb oil had weak action; 1/5 bacteria were affected and diminished the activity of other oils when tested together (40). The vapour inhibited 1/6 bacteria (42). Using the filter paper method, 14/15 bacteria were inhibited (18).

Antifungal action – No activity was noted against 12 phytopathogenic fungi and 3 wood-destroying fungi and weak activity was found against 4/15 fungi (18).
Miscellaneous action – Nil reported.

Uses

Formerly used as a urinary antiseptic (37).

DILL~   *Umbelliferae*

European Dill Herb oil/seed oil
Anethum graveolens L.

Indian Dill Seed oil
Anethum sowa Roxb.

Extraction: Steam or water distillation of whole weed or seed only.
Origin: Hungary, Finland & other European countries; India

Main components, %

	weed	Seed	Indian seed
Limonene	20-65	40-68	34-41
α-phellandrene	3-58	0.4-30	4-10
Carvone	0.2-2	54	30-49
Dihydrocarvone	1-5	0.5-5	0.1-11
Dill apiole★	0-55	20	3-67
Myristicin	0-7	0-7	trace

★3,9-oxy-p-menth-1-ene

Adulteration

Dilution with limonene, addition of carvone, caraway.

Dill oil (European) has GRAS status.

Toxicity

LD_{50} – both species 4g/kg (oral) rat; >5g/kg (dermal) rabbit.
Irritation/Sensitisation – Nil at 4%.
Phototoxicity – Nil.

Bioactivity

Pharmacology – Dill oil (European) showed an initial spasmogenic action followed by a profound spasmolytic effect on guinea-pig ileum *in vitro* (32). The spasmogenic effect was not always present. Apiole produced an increase in tone of Guinea-pig uterus; Apiole was also found to be spasmolytic on cat uterus and in high doses caused paralysis of the uterus (35).

Antibacterial action – Dill affected 5/5 bacteria (37), 18/25 different bacteria (15) and 20/25 in another study (32) and 11/20 different varieties of Listeria monocytogenes (32).The vapour affected 1/5 bacteria (42).

Antifungal action – There was a strong effect against 3/3 fungi (32). Dill seed and Dill weed oils affected 5/5 fungi but not identically (38) and 12/15 fungi (41).

Miscellaneous action – There was no antioxidant effect (32). Dill was found to be sedative according to CNV data (25.)

Uses

Dill water is used for babies to cure wind and gripes; also for adults in the treatment of stomach upsets (37).

EUCALYPTUS~   *Myrtaceae*

Eucalyptus citriodora Hooker.
Eucalyptus globulus Labill.
Eucalyptus radiata R.T. Baker

The commonest commercial Eucalyptus oil is from E.globulus, however there are over 700 species of Eucalyptus known worldwide and thousands of varieties and chemotypes are possible in this genus. Some other well-known species include: E.macurthurii; E.polybractea; E.smithii

Extraction: Steam distilled leaves and branchlets of trees.
Origin: China/Portugal/Australia.

Main components, %

	E.citriodora	E.globulus	E.radiata
1,8-Cineole	0.6	90.8	84.0
α-Pinene	0.8	6.1	1.6
Citronellal	85.0	0	0
Menthone	3.7	0	0
Citronellol	4.7	0	0
α-Terpineol	0	0	7.5
p-Cymene	0	0.8	0

E.macurthurii contains 70-80% geranyl acetate.
E.polybractea contains 90% cineole as does E.smithii.

Eucalyptus globulus oil has GRAS status; E.citriodora is acceptable in foods.

Adulteration

The main commercial Eucalyptus oils (E. globulus and E. radiata) are very cheap and therefore large-scale adulteration is not justified. However, due to the large proportion of cineole present in most commercially-produced oils, adulteration with synthetic cineole cannot be ruled out. These oils are often redistilled or rectified to give the Pharmacopoeia grade oil which has less cough-producing aldehydes and terpenes and can be used in cough medicines. Similarly, E.citriodora and E.macurthurii could be made up from their synthetic main components citronellal and geranyl acetate respectively. E.citriodora replaced citronella during the fifties(37).

Toxicity

LD_{50}

E.citriodora	>5g/kg(oral) rat,	2.5g/kg (dermal) rabbit.
E.globulus	4.4g/kg	>5g/kg.
E.radiata	not tested	not tested.

E.globulus was found to be non-teratogenic in mice (29).

Irritation/Sensitisation – E.globulus and E.citriodora nil at 10% (human), but some cases of hypersensitivity for E.globulus have been reported. "Eucalyptus" oil caused sensitivity in 3/200 dermatitis patients (50).

Phototoxicity - Nil for E.citriodora and E.globulus.

Death has occurred after an oral intake of 3.5-21 ml of Eucalyptus oil (probably E.globulus). Symptoms of poisoning included epigastric burning, nausea, vomiting, dizziness, muscular weakness, tachycardia, feeling of suffocation, delirium and convulsions (37).

Note: E.radiata and other species have not been tested for any toxicity. Oils like Ravensara aromatica which have a similar scent to E.globulus have also not been tested and as they belong to the family Lauraceae should be treated with caution.

Bioactivity

Pharmacology – E.citriodora had a very strong spasmolytic action against guinea-pig ileum *in vitro*, E.globulus showed virtually no action at the same concentration whilst E.radiata had a low spasmolytic action (32).

Antibacterial action – E.citriodora was very active against several bacteria (5). An un-named Eucalyptus oil was active against 5/5 bacteria (59) and another un-named Eucalyptus oil against 11/25 different bacteria (15). Rectified Eucalyptus oil vapour was active against 2/5 bacteria. Recent studies (32) showed that E.citriodora was very active against 10/25 bacteria and 20/20 Listeria monocytogenes varieties; E.globulus against 14/25 bacteria and 6/20 Listeria and E.radiata against 21/25 bacteria and 20/20 Listeria. This indicates that the commonest commercial oil is not as potent as other Eucalyptus oils.

Antifungal action – Five types of Eucalyptus oils were active against 5/5 fungi (38) and an unspecified oil against 4/5 fungi (42); E. citriodora was very active against 3/3 fungi whilst E. globulus and E. radiata were very ineffective at the same concentration (32). An unspecified Eucalyptus oil had low activity against 15 fungi, whilst its main component cineole was active only against 11/15 fungi (41). E.citriodora was very effective against Candida (5).

Miscellaneous action – Eucalyptus citriodora, E. globulus and E. radiata oils had no antioxidant action (32) "Eucalyptus" was a stimulant according to CNV results (25).

Uses

Eucalyptus oils (probably referring to E. globulus) are used in catarrhal conditions of the respiratory tract and given by mouth on a sugar lump or as an emulsion with olive oil. Pastilles are made together with menthol. Eucalyptus oil can also be inhaled with steam with/without menthol, pine oil, or benzoin tincture, or used in "dry" inhalers mixed with menthol, camphor, pine oils etc. Oily solutions used in the past are not recommended as they cause damage to ciliary movement and cause lipoid pneumonia. A 1% ointment for rhinitis and a 25% liniment as a rubifacient is also used (37).

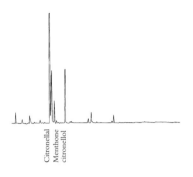

Eucalyptus Citriodora

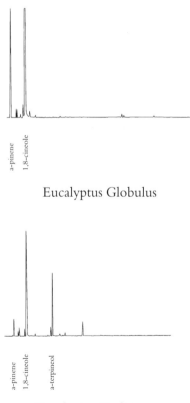

Eucalyptus Globulus

Eucalyptus Radiata

FENNEL~ *Umbelliferae*

Sweet Fennel
Foeniculum vulgare Miller subsp.capillaceum (Galib.) Holmboe var.dulce Miller

Bitter Fennel
var.vulgare Miller

Extraction: Steam distillation of seeds of plants.
Origin: Spain, E. Europe.

Main components, %

Trans–anethole	30–75
cis–anethole	0–0.3
Fenchone	10–25
Methyl chavicol	1–5
Limonene	1–55
α–pinene	1.5–15

Sweet Fennel has GRAS status.

Adulteration

Sweet Fennel, which is more important in the Fragrance industry, is often adulterated with Bitter Fennel. Various synthetic components may also be used eg. trans–anethole, fenchone, methyl chavicol and limonene. Fractions containing these components from natural essential oils are also used.

Toxicity

LD_{50} –
Bitter Fennel Seed oil: 4.5g/kg (oral) rat; >5g/kg (dermal) rabbit.
Sweet Fennel Seed oil: 3.8g/kg (oral) rat; >5g/kg (dermal) rabbit.
Irritation/Sensitisation – Both Bitter and Sweet Fennel seed oil: nil at 4% (human). However, Sweet Fennel applied undiluted to mice proved severely irritating and to rabbit skin was moderately irritating. Anethole has reportedly allergenic properties and is toxic.
Phototoxicity – Nil.

Bioactivity

Pharmacology – Sweet Fennel Seed oil had a strong spasmogenic action on the smooth muscle of the guinea-pig ileum *in vitro*, which was followed by a spasmolytic action (32). Fennel oil is stated to be oestrogenic (2).
Antibacterial action – Was very low; using an unspecified Fennel 3/5

bacteria were affected (59) and 6/25 different bacteria were affected in one study (15), and, using Sweet Fennel, 6/25 in another (32). Sweet Fennel vapour affected only 1/5 bacteria (42).

Antifungal action – Fennel was poor against 4/5 fungi and good against one of them (38) and in another study using Sweet Fennel, action was very good against 1/3 fungi and moderate against the other two (32). Fennel affected 11/15 fungi (41).

Miscellaneous action – No antioxidant action was found in Sweet Fennel (32).

Uses

Fennel oil is used as a carminative especially for children (37)

FRANKINCENSE~   *Burseracae*
syn. Olibanum
Boswellia carterii birdw.

Extraction: Steam distilled oleo-gum-resin from trees obtained as tear drops or differently-shaped lumps from lesions in the bark.
Origin: Eritrea, India, Aden.

Main components, %

α-Pinene	1.0	(to 43% Aden)
α-Thujene	0-2	(to 61% Indian)
p-Cymene	0.1	(to 8% Aden)
linalool	0.2	(to 3% Eritrea)
n-Octyl acetate	0-5	(>52% Eritrea)
n-Octanol	0-4	(8% Eritrea)

Profound differences in composition occur between resins from Aden, Eritrea and India. The CMA International grading is based on the pinene content: Grade 1 = 37-42%, but the Indian variety is very pleasant and yet contains very little pinene.

Can be used in foods.

Adulteration

Many of the components are added as synthetics, in particular α-pinene. The quality of the oils vary according to both source and method of extraction.

Toxicity

LD_{50} –
>5g/kg (oral) rat; >5g/kg (dermal) rabbit.
Irritation/Sensitisation – Nil at 8%.
Phototoxicity – Untested.

Bioactivity

Pharmacology – A strong spasmogenic action was produced in guinea-pig ileum *in vitro* (32).
Antibacterial action – Frankincense had a very strong action against 23/25 different bacteria and 18/25 Listeria monocytogenes varieties (32).
Antifungal action – Was poor against 5/5 fungi (38) and also poor against 3/3 fungi (32).
Miscellaneous action – No antioxidant effect was found (32).

GERANIUM~ *Geraniaceae*

Pelargonium cultivars eg. cv. Rose

Derived from P.graveolens, P.radens, P.capitatum
and other species originating in South Africa

Note: not to be confused with the true geranium oil from Geranium
macrorrhizum known as Zdravetz oil, produced in Bulgaria - which is
totally different in composition and odour.

Extraction: Steam-distilled leaves of plants.
Origin: Reunion (Bourbon)/China/Egypt/Morocco.

Main components, %

Citronellol	28-48
Geraniol	7-19
Linalool	3-10
Isomenthone	4-7
Citronellyl formate	5-12
Geranyl formate	1-4

(Data are based on analysis of 40 commercial Geranium oils (22,25), but
the ISO stipulates a citronellol content of: Minimum 42%/Maximum
55% for Bourbon; 35/58 for Morocco and 40/58 for Egypt and 40/58
for China.

Minor components
10-epi-g-eudesmol 3-7% in Egypt and Morocco oils
guaia-6,9-diene 1-7% in Bourbon and China oils
Geranium oil has GRAS status.

Adulteration

There is substantial adulteration of Geranium oils due to the increasing
price and scarcity of raw material. Many oils are produced from synthetic
components and many are adjusted to the required standards with
synthetics. The most expensive Geranium oil was Bourbon and many
producers round the world tried to imitate this particular oil, especially
China, resulting in a massive and unbelievable increase of Bourbon from
the tiny mountainous island of Reunion!

Toxicity

LD_{50}

Bourbon	>5g/kg (oral) rat	2.5g/kg (dermal) rabbit.
Moroccan	not tested	>5g/kg .

Other oils not tested.

It may be more relevant to know the toxicity of the main components (citronellol, geraniol, linalool and citronellyl formate) which all showed a very non-toxic LD_{50} of >5g/kg (oral) rat and >5g/kg (dermal) rabbit. *Irritation/Sensitisation* – Nil for Bourbon and Moroccan at 10%.

Note: There are a few reports of dermatitis in hypersensitive individuals especially when picking the leaves of unspecified pelargoniums and 3/200 dermatitis patients were sensitive to Geranium oil (50).
Phototoxicity – Nil reported.

Bioactivity

Pharmacology – There was a spasmolytic action on guinea-pig ileum *in vitro* (31,34) by 40 Geranium oil samples. However, P.grossularioides was unusual in being spasmogenic; this species has been used as an abortifacient in Southern African Folk Medicine (30) – however commercial Geranium oils are never produced from this species.

Antibacterial action – Was very variable: 19/25 bacteria were affected by a sample of Geranium oil (15) whilst 8-19/25 different bacteria were affected by 16 different samples of Geranium oil and 3-14/20 Listeria monocytogenes varieties (32). Different Pelargonium species and cultivars also had differing effects on 25 bacteria varieties (33). Algerian Geranium oil was active against 5/5 bacteria (41) and the vapour against 1/5 bacteria (42).

Antifungal action – Four different Geranium oils were active against 5/5 fungi (38); there was also good activity against 3 fungi by 16 samples of Geranium oils (31,34). Algerian oil showed activity against 12/15 fungi (41) and fungistatic activity against Candida albicans and Trichophyton mentagrophytes (24).

Miscellaneous action – A sedative action was found for Geranium oil according to CNV data (25). Geranium oils also have an insecticidal action: many different species and cultivars were very potent insecticides when fed to insects (29). Antioxidant values were very variable in 16 samples of Geranium oil studied ranging from nil to very potent (31,34).

Uses

Geranium oil dabbed on the skin undiluted is an effective mosquito repellent (personal observations).

Note: A large number of medicinal properties have been assigned erroneously to Geranium oil owing to the misinterpretation of the botanical origin of the oil eg. Culpepper's Herbal (14) is often quoted BUT the species referred to are the hardy Geraniums growing wild in

Europe (e.g. G. Robertianum or Herb Robert) and not the Pelargonium species originating in Southern Africa.

Studies based on the major components of Geranium oil have established that there is a maximum acceptable daily intake of up to 500μg per kg body weight of citral, geranyl acetate, citronellol, linalool (37).

GINGER~
Zingiberaceae

Zingiber officinale Roscoe

Extraction: Steam distillation of the dried, ground rhizome.
Origin: India, China, Africa, Australia.

Main components, %

1,8-Cineole	1-11
Geranial	tr-27
α,β-Zingiberene	2-51
ar-Curcumene	0.1-33
Linalool	1-5
β-Sesquiphellandrene	0-11

Ginger oil has GRAS status

Adulteration

Galanga oil can be used as an adulterant, but generally there is ample supply of ginger therefore substitutions are rare, with differences occurring mainly between ginger oils from different countries and mode of distillation.

Toxicity

LD_{50} – >5g/kg (oral) rat; >5g/kg (dermal) rabbit.
Irritation/Sensitisation – Nil at 4% (human). Ginger oil-containing products may cause dermatitis in hypersensitive people.
Phototoxicity – Very minor effect.

Bioactivity

Pharmacology – Very slight spasmolytic action on guinea-pig ileum *in vitro* (personal observation).
Antibacterial action – Was low; 7/25 bacteria were affected (15).
Ginger oil had no effect on 5/5 Listeria monocytogenes varieties (6).
1/5 bacteria were affected by Ginger oil vapour (42).
Antifungal action – Was virtually absent, no action was found against 5 fungi (38) and fungistatic action alone was found against 8/15 fungi (41).
Miscellaneous action – Nil reported.

Uses

Ginger is a carminative and is sometimes also added to purgatives in the belief that it prevents griping (37).

HO LEAF~   *Lauraceae*
Cinnamomum camphora L. Nees & Ebermeier
C. camphora Sieb.

Extraction: Steam distillation of leaves of tree.
Origin: Japan, Brazil.

Main components, %

Linalool	85-95
Linalyl acetate	2-5
Terpenes (various) at 0.1-0.5 levels	

Ho-leaf oil is temporarily included in the List for Food Use.

Adulteration

Synthetic Linalool with Linalyl acetate is often used.

Note: There is a very close similarity with Rosewood oil, and this makes the substitution of Ho wood leaves for Rosewood a good prospect on environmentally-friendly grounds.

Toxicity

LD_{50} – 3.8g/kg (oral) rat; >5g/kg (dermal) rabbit.
Irritation/Sensitisation – Nil at 10% (human).
Phototoxicity – Not tested.

Bioactivity

Pharmacology – A spasmolytic effect was produced on guinea-pig ileum in vitro (32).
Antibacterial action – 23/25 different bacteria were affected and 15/20 Listeria monocytogenes varieties (32).
Antifungal action – There was a strong action against 3/3 fungi (32).
Miscellaneous action – There was an antioxidant effect (32).

JASMINE~   *Oleaceae*

Jasminum grandiflorum L.
(often grafted onto J.officinalis)

Extraction: solvent extraction of flowers, hand-picked at dawn.
Origin: Egypt, India.

Main components, %

Benzyl benzoate	11.5
Benzyl acetate	25.8
Linalool	4.6
Indole	3.7
Eugenol	2.6
cis-Jasmone	2.4
Farnesene	2.0
Phytols	27.9

Jasmine has GRAS status

Adulteration

Due to the high price of the authentic oil, many imitations are made. Adulterations are made with indole, cinnamic aldehyde, ylang ylang fractions etc.

Toxicity

LD_{50} – >5g/kg (oral)rat, >5g/kg (dermal) rabbit.
Irritation/Sensitisation – Nil at 3% (human).
Phototoxicity – Nil reported.

Bioactivity

Pharmacology – A spasmolytic effect was produced on guinea-pig ileum *in vitro* (32.
Antibacterial action – Nil reported.
Antifungal action – Nil reported.
Miscellaneous action – Stimulant activity was reported according to CNV data (36,57).

JUNIPER~   *Cupressaceae*
Juniperus communis L.

Extraction: Steam distillation of crushed dried berries of tree. Major production from fermented Juniper berries from Gin and brandy manufacture, the distillate being separated off from the alcohol.
Origin: Hungary and other E. European countries.

Main components, %

α-Pinene	33-71
Sabinene	0.3-27
Myrcene	5-18
Limonene	2-9
γ-Terpinene	0.3-3.7
Terpinen-4-ol	4-10

Juniper Berry oil has GRAS status.

Adulteration
True Juniper berry oil is rare and the fermented oil is usually sold. Many components can be added e.g. pinene, camphene, myrcene and turpentine oil fractions etc. Juniper wood oil and Juniper twig oil, also oil of Juniperus smreka, are often added as adulterants.

Toxicity
LD_{50} – 8g/kg (oral)rat; >5g/kg (dermal) rabbit.
Irritation/Sensitisation – Nil at 8% (human). Tested at 100% on 20 volunteers for 24 hours, produced irritation in 2 cases.
Phototoxicity – nil.

Bioactivity
Pharmacology – A small spasmolytic effect was produced by Juniper berry oil (32).
Antibacterial action – Nil reported.
Antifungal action – A twice rectified Juniper oil had no effect on 5/5 fungi (38). Juniper berry oil affected 6/15 fungi while Juniper tar affected 13/15 fungi (41).
Miscellaneous action – Nil reported.

Uses
Juniper oil is a carminative, and is used for flatulence and colic; it is also used as a diuretic, but not for those with renal disease; dose – 0.05-0.2ml (37).

LAVENDER~ *Labiatiae*

Lavandin - Lavandula augustifolia P.Miller
x Lavandula latifolia (L.) Medikus
Lavender - Lavandula augustifolia P.Miller
syn. Lavandula officinalis (Chaiz.)
Spike Lavender - Lavandula latifolia Vill.
    syn.L.spica (D.C.)

Extraction: Steam distilled flowering tops.
Origin: France/Bulgaria, France/Spain respectively

Major components, %

	Lavandin	*Lavender*	*Spike*
Linalool	24-41	6-50	11-54
Linalyl Acetate	2-34	7-56	0.8-15
1,8-Cineole	6-26	0-5	25-37
Lavandulol	0.8-1.4	0-7	0.3-0.7
Lavandulyl Acetate	<3.5	5-30	0
Camphor	0.4-12	0-0.8	9-60

Minor components: cis-ocimene, trans-ocimene, 3-octanone are often used as markers of authenticity of Lavender oil together with the ratios of the main components:

$$\frac{cis\text{-}ocimene}{trans\text{-}ocimene} = 1.08 - 2.66$$

$$\frac{trans\text{-}ocimene}{3\text{-}octanone} = 0.36 - 4.33$$

$$\frac{linalool + linalyl\ acetate}{lavandulol + lavandulyl\ acetate} = 10.4 - 27.59$$

Lavender also has borneol to 1.8% but no bornyl acetate whilst Lavandin has 2.9-3.7% of the latter and nil of the former.

All three Lavenders have GRAS status.

Adulteration

The ISO stipulates that Lavender oil should contain a minimum of 25% and a maximum of 45% Linalyl acetate and 25% and 38% Linalool respectively. This encourages adulteration of Lavender oils by cutting with acetylated Lavandin oil, synthetic Linalool and Linalyl acetate, fractions of Ho Leaf oil and Rosewood oil (Bois de Rose); the last two consist largely of Linalool and its acetate but are much cheaper. Lavandin, which is much cheaper than Lavender is often substituted for the latter.

Toxicity

LD₅₀

Lavandin and Lavender − >5g/kg (oral) rat; >5g/kg (dermal) rabbit.
Spike lavender − 4 g/kg (oral) rat;   >2g/kg (dermal) rabbit.
Irritation /Sensitisation − Lavandin − nil at 5% (human).
                                          Lavender − Nil at 10%.
                                          Spike − Nil at 8 %.

1/200 dermatitis patients was sensitive to Lavandin and 1/200 to Spike
Lavender (50).
Phototoxicity − Nil reported.

Bioactivity

Pharmacology − Different Lavenders gave mostly a spasmolytic effect on
guinea-pig ileum *in vitro*, but a spasmogenic effect was found initially in
4/7 samples (32). In dogs, there was an increase in tone and rhythmic
contractions and peristalsis *in vivo* (44).

Antibacterial action − Was variable; there was action against 3/5 bacteria
(59) and the vapour against 1/5 bacteria for Lavender; Lavandin vapour
affected 1/5 and Spike oil vapour 2/5 whilst acetylated Spike was less
active against 1/5 (42) and 18/25 bacteria studied (15). Different
lavenders showed activity against 14-24/25 different bacteria and 3-
16/20 Listeria monocytogenes varieties; Spike lavender was active against
20/25 bacteria and 12/20 Listeria (32).

Antifungal action − Generally is low: Lavandin and Lavender were active
against 5/5 fungi, but some activities were low (38); Lavender was also
found to be active against 5/5 different fungi, with mainly low effects
(59); different Lavenders and Lavandins showed from poor to good effect
on 3 fungi similarly to Spike Lavender (32).

Miscellaneous action − Lavender was found to be a sedative in mice (10) and
humans (12). The CNV data in man also shows its sedative action (25,57).
There was some antioxidant effect in some of the Lavenders and Lavandin
samples tested whilst no activity was found in Spike Lavender (32).

Uses

Lavender is reportedly a healing oil and can be applied to the skin on open
wounds undiluted (Gattefosse); the use of deterpenated oil was advised
for maximum benefit. Lavender oil has carminative properties and has
been used to treat flatulence and colic, given on a sugar lump (dose 0.3-
1.2ml or as a compound tincture. Lavender oil is also applied externally
as an insect repellant (37).

The maximum acceptable daily intake of the components Linalool and
Linalyl acetate were established at 500μg per kg body weight per day (37).

LEMON~   *Rutaceae*
Citrus limonum (L.) Burm.f.
syn. C.limonum Risso.

Extraction: Expressed oil from lemon peel
Origin: Sicily,California USA, Argentina,Spain.

Main components, %

Limonene	66-80
α-pinene	1-4
β-pinene	0.4-15
γ-terpinene	6-14
Geranial	1-3
Neral	0.2-1.3
Myrcene	0-13
p-cymene	0-2
α-bergamotene	0-2.5

Minor components

Furocoumarins or bergaptens (see below and Bergamot).

Lemon oil has GRAS status.

Adulteration

Citrus oils are often "folded" – this entails the evaporation of some terpenes with heat under mild vacuum and gives 5,10,20,40 etc. folded oils. Other volatile components are lost. Citrus oils are also "washed" by partitioning the oil into a mixture of alcohol and water and stirring for 24 hours. Folding and washing can be jointly used . Other deterpenation methods involve chromatographic separations and countercurrent deterpenations. Thus, a multitude of different oils is possible. (See also Orange oil).

Frequently adulterated with distilled Lemon oil, concentrated Lemon oil from vacuum distilled Lemon oil, terpeneless or sesquiterpeneneless Lemon oils; synthetic limonene, citral, dipentene etc can also be added. Adulteration is very difficult to detect using conventional gas chromatography analysis. Citral from Lemongrass can be added, also turpentine. As Lemon oil is ten times more expensive than Orange oil, the latter and its products are often blended in. Antioxidants like BHT and BHA are frequently added to prevent oxidation of the citrus oils and prolong shelf-life.

Toxicity

LD_{50} – >5g/kg (oral) rat; >5g/kg (dermal) rabbit.

Irritation/Sensitisation – Nil at 10% and nil at 100%. 1/200 dermatitis patients were sensitive to Lemon oil (50).

Phototoxicity – High to low levels of photoxicity , depending on the actual chemical composition of the oil and sensitivity of the user (see Bergamot).

Bioactivity

Pharmacology – There was a strong spasmogenic action on guinea-pig ileum *in vitro* (32).

Antibacterial action – Was generally poor: 9/25 bacteria were affected (15), 4/5 bacteria affected (38) and 8/25 different bacteria and 3/20 Listeria monocytogenes varieties affected (32), whilst in another study Lemon oil was ineffective against 5/5 Listeria (6).

Antifungal action – Showed different effects: 5/5 fungi were affected (38) and nil to a very poor effect was noted on 3/3 fungi (32).

Miscellaneous action – Lemon oil was said to be a sedative according to decreased CNV (36). No antioxidant effect was noted (32). Lemon oil relieved depression when sprayed near patients (49).

A preparation of D-Limonene has been used for dissolving gall stones (37).

LEMONGRASS~   *Graminae*
Cymbopogon citratus L.
syn. C, flexuosus (Nees) Stapf.
syn. Andropogon nardus var. Flexuosus

Extraction: Steam distilled or Steam/water distilled fresh or partly dried leaves of the grass.
Origin: Cochin, Guatemala

Main components, %

Geranial	45-87	} citral
Neral	25-40	
Myrcene	0.5-19	
Limonene	0-2.4	
Geraniol	0.5-16	

Lemongrass has GRAS status.

Adulteration

This is one of the cheapest oils and is therefore unlikely to be adulterated with synthetic citral. Litsea cubeba oil has a similar citral content and could be used as a substitute where it is grown as in China. Lemongrass itself is a useful supplier of citral which is used for the production of vitamin A and ionones. A common substitute is Jammu oil (C.pendulus Nees ex.Stend) which contains 75-80% citral.

Toxicity

LD_{50} –
East Indian > 5g/kg (oral) rat; >2g/kg (dermal) rabbit.
West Indian > 5g/kg (oral) rat; >5g/kg.
Irritation and Sensitisation – Nil at 4% (human).
Phototoxicity – Nil reported.

Bioactivity

Pharmacology – There was a strong spasmolytic effect on guinea-pig ileum *in vitro* (23,26)
Antibacterial action – Potent against one bacterium but not another (5); 18/25 bacteria and 20/20 Listeria monocytogenes varieties were affected (32). Rectified Lemongrass vapour was active against 4/5 bacteria (42).
Antifungal action – Shown by rectified Lemongrass oil against 5/5 fungi (38), and moderate to good action against 3 fungi by commercial Lemongrass oil (32). Lemongrass oil was effective against Tinea and Dandruff (5). Lemongrass oil was active against 11/15 fungi (41).

Miscellaneous action – There was a small rise in the CNV indicating a stimulant action (36,57). There was some antioxidant activity (32).

Uses

Lemongrass is used as an insect repellent, but is not as good as conventional products (37). It was also used in the past as a carminative.

LITSEA~ *Lauraceae*

Litsea cubeba L.
May Chang tree

Extraction: steam distillation of pepper-like fruits of tree.
Origin: China, Formosa

Main components, %

Geranial	40.6
Neral	33.8
α-Pinene	0.9
β-Pinene	0.4
Myrcene	3.0
Citronellal	0.6

Adulteration

As the oil is very similar in citral levels to Lemongrass, substitution by the latter is likely. Litsea citrata planted as wind-breaker in Chinese teagroves may also be used but has a lower citral level. Litsea is a cheap oil, therefore, citral is uneconomical as an adulterant.

Toxicity

LD_{50} – >5g/kg (oral) rat; >5g/kg (dermal) rabbit.
Irritation/Sensitisation – Nil at 8% (human). In dermatitis patients, 3/200 and 13/450 patients were affected at 2% (50).
Phototoxicity – Not tested.

Bioactivity

Pharmacology – A spasmolytic effect was found on guinea-pig ileum *in vitro* (32). When administered intraperitoneally or by inhalation to guinea-pigs, it protected them against asthma induced by inhaled bronchoconstrictors. The oil also inhibited passive cutaneous anaphylaxis in rats and anaphylactic shock in guinea-pigs sensitised to egg albumen (18).
Antibacterial action – Was found against 16-18/25 bacteria and 18-20/20 Listeria monocytogenes varieties (32).
Antifungal action – Was demonstrated against 3/3 fungi at poor to good level for different Litsea samples (32).
Miscellaneous action: No antioxidant activity was found (32).

MARJORAM~
Labiatiae

Sweet and French Marjoram
Majorana hortensis Moench.
syn.Origanum majorana L.

Spanish marjoram
Thymus capitatus L.
Origanum virens L.
O.vulgare L.
Thymus mastichina L.

Extraction: Steam distillation of the leaves and flowering tops of plants.
Origin: France, Spain.

Main components, %

	French	Spanish
1,8-Cineole	0 -58	50 -62
α-Terpinene	0	1 -4
γ-Terpinene	3 -16	0.4 -5
Terpinolene	13 -19	10 -20
α-Terpineol	2 -6	2 -4
Terpinen-4-ol	0 -30	0
β-Caryophyllene	0 -2	0 -2

There is a wide variation in Marjoram oils due to the numerous chemotypes as well as different species.

Sweet Marjoram has GRAS status.

Adulteration

Usually Tea Tree oil is used or the terpenes from deterpenation of other oils and mixing or substitution by Spanish for French oil, Origanum or Thymes etc.

Toxicity

LD_{50} – 2.2g/kg (oral) rat; >5g/kg (dermal)rabbit.
Irritation/Sensitisation – Nil at 6% (Human).
Phototoxicity – Not tested for Sweet Marjoram, but nil for Spanish Marjoram.

Bioactivity

Pharmacology – There was a slight spasmolytic effect on guinea-pig ileum *in vitro* (32).

71

Antibacterial action – A Marjoram oil was very active against 24/25 different bacteria (15) and samples of Sweet, French and Spanish Marjoram oils were active against 23-25/25 bacteria and 15-20/20 Listeria monocytogenes varieties (32). However, in another study there was no activity for a Marjoram oil against 5/5 Listeria (6). Sweet Marjoram vapour was active against 2/5 bacteria (42).

Antifungal action – Sweet Marjoram was moderately active against 5/5 fungi (38). There was from a very low to moderate effect on 3/3 fungi by various Sweet, French and Spanish Marjoram oils (32). Sweet Marjoram was active against 15/15 fungi (41).

Miscellaneous action – There was a varied antioxidant effect of Spanish, French and Sweet Marjoram oils giving from nil to strong activity (32). Marjoram has sedative properties according to CNV data (59).

MELISSA~ *Labiatiae*
Lemon Balm
Melissa officinalis L.

Extraction: Steam distillation of leaves and tops of herb
Origin: France

Main components, %

β-Caryophyllene   11.7, 29.0
Geranial   25.0, 17.3
Neral   15.3, 10.9
Citronellal   24.6, 2.2
Humulene   0, 2.1
γ-Cadinene   0, 2.1

Note: The data above refer to two laboratory distilled Melissa oils, but the commercial oils are very variable due to massive adulteration.

Melissa oil has GRAS status.

Adulteration

Due to the low yield and high cost of the pure oil (comparable to the cost of Rose oil), most commercial Melissa oils are compounded from synthetic components. The Lemon Balm may be distilled with Lemon oil, Verbena oil, Lemongrass, Citronella and mixtures of these or their various fractions. The properties of Melissa oil given below most probably refer to commercial oils.

Toxicity

LD_{50} – No data available.
Irritation/Sensitisation – No data available.
Phototoxicity – No data available.

Bioactivity

Pharmacology – A commercial sample of oil was weakly spasmolytic on guinea-pig ileum *in vitro* (32).
Antibacterial action – A commercial sample of Melissa oil was active against 22/25 bacteria and 9/20 Listeria monocytogenes varieties (32) Melissa oil was also active against 9/25 bacteria (15). The vapour was active against 1/5 bacteria (42).
Antifungal action – A commercial sample of Melissa oil was moderately active against 3/3 fungi (32).
Miscellaneous action – A commercial sample had very strong antioxidant

properties (32). Melissa oil was found to be a relaxant based on its CNV effects (57).

Note: Many erroneous quotations have been made as to the anti-viral properties of Melissa oil due to the misinterpretation of scientific reports. The anti-viral properties in Melissa are in the tannins (21), which are water-soluble components and therefore are <u>not</u> present in the essential oil fraction.

Uses

Melissa herb (as dried leaves made into a tea) has been used as a carminative and general relaxant and the dried leaves are used in herbal pillows to induce relaxing sleep.

MINTS~ *Labiatiae*

Peppermint – Mentha x piperita L.
   Hybrid of M.spicata x M. aquatica L.

Spearmint – Mentha spicata L.
   related to M. viridis and Na` na of Mediterranean

Cornmint – Mentha arvensis var.piperascens Holmes
Scotch Peppermint – M. cardiaca (Baker) Gerarde or M.x gracilis Sole, with a high carvone content is sometimes used.

Extraction: Steam distilled flowering tops, partly dried
Origin: USA

Main components, %

	Peppermint	*Spearmint*	*Cornmint*
Menthol	27 -51	0.1 -0.3	65 -80 (38)
Menthone	13 -32	0.7 -2	3.4 -15 (31)
Isomenthone	2 -10	trace	1.9 -4.8 (12)
1,8-Cineole	5 -14	1 -2	0.1 -0.3 (0.2-0.8)
Limonene	1 -3	8 -12	0.7 -6.2 (10)
Carvone	0	58 -70	0

(Brackets indicate values in dementholised Cornmint)

Minor components
Menthofuran (2-12%) occurs in Peppermint only and this is removed partly by rectification to improve the taste of the oil. This is used as a guide to purity but see below!

Peppermint and Spearmint have GRAS status but not Cornmint.

Adulteration

Peppermint oil is the most adulterated oil. Most often the cheaper Cornmint is used as a diluent or substitute for Peppermint oil; it is often difficult to detect adulteration even at 85% Cornmint addition as the colour test for menthofuran remains the same. Cornmint is often mixed with the inferior fore-runs of Peppermint which also results in a positive menthofuran test.

Toxicity

LD_{50} – Peppermint   4.4g/kg (oral) rat.
         Cornmint   1.2g/kg (oral) rat.
         Spearmint   untested.
Irritation/Sensitisation – Peppermint – can be an irritant and may cause

allergic reactions. Not only heartburn has been reported but a few drops of the oil taken on a sugar lump can almost cause asphyxiation due to the sharpness of the odour and effect on the nose and throat. Allergic reactions have been reported after massive oral intakes of peppermint flavoured sweets and toothpaste. Idiopathic auricular fibrillation occurred in two patients addicted to mint sweets – normal rhythm was restored after they ceased to eat the mints. An acute allergic response occurred in the mouth, neck and throat of a sensitive person when using toothpaste flavoured with peppermint (18,37). It is considered generally safe at 4%. Spearmint – Nil at 4% but there was 1 case of allergic response due to flavoured toothpaste. 0.1% is recommended for hypersensitive people. 1/200 patients were sensitive to peppermint (50).

Phototoxicity – Nil reported.

Bioactivity

Pharmacology – Peppermint and Spearmint, used in a watery dilution, caused relaxation of the gastric wall and decrease in contractions, but caused an increase in tone and contractions in the ileum and colon of dogs (47). Peppermint was found to be antispasmodic in the mouse intestine (20) and guinea-pig ileum (32) *in vitro*.

Antibacterial action – was very variable for Peppermint oil 3/5 bacteria were affected(38); 19/25 were affected (15) and 5/5 Listeria monocytogenes varieties were limited by Peppermint oil from Piedmont (6). Peppermint oil vapour was active against 3/5 bacteria while the rectified peppermint vapour against 2/5 and Spearmint vapour against 1/5 bacteria (42).

Antifungal action – Showed variability: Peppermint oil affected 3/5 fungi (38); and a sample of Peppermint oil affected 3/3 fungi (32). There was low activity against 15/15 fungi (41).

Miscellaneous action – "Mint" was used in an aerosol for controlling epilepsy in patients (49). No antioxidant action was found (32).

Uses

Peppermint is a licensed essential oil which can be used medicinally in this country. It is used for dyspepsia, bronchitis and in particular irritable bowel syndrome (16,37,48). Administration of enteric-coated capsules (Colpermin or Mintec) can deliver the oil to the colon without causing an irritant effect on the upper respiratory system and upper digestive system. Peppermint oil can reduce colonic spasm during endoscopy when introduced together with the colonoscope. It is also good as a local anaesthetic and counterirritant for muscular aches and pains (37).

MYRRH~ *Burseraceae*

Commiphora myrrha (Nees) Engler
syn.C.abyssinica (Berg) Engler
syn.C.myrrha var. molmol Engler
syn.molmol Engler.

Extraction: Steam distilled crude Myrrh also Myrrh absolute from ethanolic extract of resinoid.
Origin: Somalia, Eritrea, Yemen, Saudi Arabia.

Main components, %

Curzerene   11.9
Furanoeudesma-1-3-diene 12.5
Curzerenone   11.7
Lindestrene   3.5

Adulteration

Often contaminated with Opoponax. Myrrh extractives using solvents are often referred to as the oil after decolourisation.

Toxicity

LD_{50} – Myrrh oil -1.7g/kg (oral) rat; Dermal not tested.
Myrrh absolute – not tested.
Irritation/Sensitisation – Myrrh oil – Nil at 8%.
Myrrh absolute – Nil at 8%, but cross-sensitisation reaction occurred in a patient who developed contact dermatitis after exposure to benzoin.
Phototoxicity – Not tested.

Bioactivity

Pharmacology – A strong spasmogenic reaction was found on the guinea-pig ileum *in vitro* (32).
Antibacterial action – Was very poor: 6/25 different bacteria were affected and 6/20 Listeria monocytogenes varieties (32).
Antifungal action – Was extremely poor or non-existent against 3/3 fungi (32) and 13/15 fungi (41).
Miscellaneous action – Myrrh oil has no antioxidant properties (32).

Myrrh has a historical use in fragrances and in ceremonial and religious festivities where it was burnt together with other spices and essential oils. It was used for embalming and given as a precious gift e.g. at the First Christmas, together with gold and frankincense.

NEROLI~ *Rutaceae*

Citrus aurantium L.
Citrus bigaradia L.

Extraction: Steam distillation of the blossom of citrus tree.
Origin: Italy, France, Morocco, Tunisia.

Main components, %

Linalool	23.8
Linalyl acetate	68.5
Geraniol	5.9
Limonene	trace

The composition of pure Neroli oil differs markedly from the many imitations on the market. Some "Neroli" oil consist almost exclusively of linalyl acetate.

Neroli oil has GRAS status.

Adulteration

Artificial Neroli oil abounds due to the high cost of the genuine oil. Petitgrain oil is often a substitute, or some of the Petitgrain terpenoids, Bitter Orange oil, synthetic linalool, linalyl acetate, nerol, nerolidol, phenylethyl alcohol, decanal, nonanal, isojasmone etc.

Toxicity

LD_{50} – 4.5g/kg (oral) rat; >5g/kg (dermal) rabbit.
Irritation/Sensitisation – Nil at 4% (human). When applied undiluted to mice and swine, no irritation was produced.
Phototoxicity – Nil.

Bioactivity

Antibacterial action – Neroli oil was 5.5 times more effective as a bactericide than phenol (37). Antibacterial action against 5/5 bacteria was shown (59) and the vapour was active against 1/5 bacteria (42). Two samples of commercial Neroli were very active against 20, 22/25 bacteria and 11,19/20 Listeria monocytogenes varieties (32).
Antifungal action – Moderate antifungal action was found against 13/15 fungi (38) and 11/12 phytopathogenic fungi (18), whilst another study showed that a 1; 50 dilution of Neroli bigarade petale oil had an effect on 11/12 phytopathogenic fungi (18). Two commercial Neroli oils had a moderate to good effect on 3/3 fungi (32).
Miscellaneous action – Neroli bigarade oil (10mg, as a 1 in 25 solution in

olive injected intramuscularly weekly) had a weak therapeutic effect on experimental tuberculosis of the guinea-pig when combined with subeffective doses of dihydrostreptomycin. However Neroli at 100μg/ml had no effect on the tubercle bacilli *in vitro* (18).

NUTMEG~ *Myristicaceae*
Myristica fragrans Houtt.

Extraction: Steam distillation of freshly-comminuted dried ripe seeds.
Origin: Indonesia, Ceylon (East Indian), Papua, West Indies.

Main components, %

	West Indian	East Indian
α-Pinene	10.6 -13.2	19.2 -26.5
β-Pinene	7.8 -12.1	9.7 -17.7
Sabinene	43.0 -50.7	15.4 -36.3
Myrcene	3.5 -3.4	2.2 -3.7
α-Terpinene	0.8 -4.2	0.8 -4.0
Limonene	3.1 -4.4	2.7 -3.6
1,8-Cineole	2.3 -4.2	1.5 -3.2
γ-Terpinene	1.9 -4.7	1.9 -6.8
Terpinen-4-ol	3.5 -6.1	2.0 -10.9
Elemicin	1.2 -1.4	0.3 -4.6
Myristicin	0.5 -0.9	3.3 -13.5

The East Indian nutmeg is generally preferred by perfumers. Terpeneless oil is also produced.

Mace is the dried finger-like, husk-like arillode surrounding the nutmeg seed inside the fruit shell. It is nowadays not distinguishable as an oil from nutmeg oil. Some nutmegs are eaten by worms, which eat the fixed oil, glyceryl myristate, in the seed leaving the essential oil-bearing tissue intact and therefore save the producer the bother of removing the former with solvents. However, the appearance of such half-eaten nutmegs suggests both aged and badly stored nutmegs.

Nutmeg masks many odours e.g. the odour of cooked cabbage.

Nutmeg oil has GRAS status.

Adulteration

Many monoterpenes are added e.g. myrcene, camphene, terpinolene, pinene, also melaleuca alternifolia, terpenes from deterpenisation of nutmeg and myristicin from various rare plants etc.

Toxicity

LD_{50} – 0.6-2.6g/kg (oral)rat; >5g/kg mice; >5g/kg hamsters and 10g/kg (dermal) rabbit.
Irritation/Sensitisation – Nil at 2% (human).
Phototoxicity – Not tested.

Note: Nutmeg is toxic due mainly to its myristicin content (the latter is related to safrole). Nutmeg, when imbibed as a concoction made from the ground powder, causes hallucinations, visual impairments, delirium and prolonged sleep (28). Overdose of nutmeg causes nausea,vomiting, flushing, a dry mouth, epileptic-like convulsions, delirium and either acts as a Central Nervous System inhibitor or stimulant (37).

Bioactivity

Pharmacology – There was a very profound spasmogenic action on guinea-pig ileum *in vitro* (32). Myristicin given to monkeys caused ataxia and disorientation and also enhanced morphine-induced rage in cats (18).
Antibacterial action – Nutmeg oil was very effective against 5/5 bacteria (59), also 18,19/25 bacteria were affected by two different samples of Nutmeg oil and 0,12/20 Listeria monocytogenes varieties (32). The vapours of East and West Indian Nutmeg oils were active only against 1/5 bacteria (42).
Antifungal action – Nil to good effects were noted against 5/5 different fungi (41) by 2 samples of Nutmeg oil, poor to moderate action against 3/3 fungi was found by two samples of Nutmeg oil (32).
Miscellaneous action – Moderate to good antioxidant activity was found for two samples of Nutmeg oil (32).

Uses

Nutmeg oil and its myristicin and elemicin components have been patented for their soothing effects on man. Nutmeg oil has carminative properties; 10% oil in alcohol (spirits) are taken at 0.3/1.2ml. The oil is also used as a rubefacient (37). Nutmeg inhibits prostaglandin synthesis and there are reports of successful treatment of diarrhoea associated with increased plasma prostaglandin levels with nutmeg (37). Nutmeg oil inhibits platelet aggregation *in vitro*, and thus, in theory could prevent coronaries (51). Nutmeg has also been used in veterinary medicine and as a medicine for various conditions but in particular for diarrhoea (52), where the active component was identified as eugenol, which is also the main constituent of cloves (8).

ORANGE~   *Rutaceae*

Sweet Orange oil
    Citrus sinensis (L.) Osbeck
    syn.C.aurantium L.var.sinensis L./var.dulcis L.
Bitter Orange oil
    Citrus aurantium L. subsp. amara

Extraction: Expressed oil from orange peel.
Origin: Brazil, Florida USA, Mexico, Argentina, Indonesia.

Main components, %

	Sweet	Bitter
Limonene	94 -98	73 -98
Myrcene	1.6	1 -11
α-Pinene	0.4	0.3 -1.4
Sabinene	0.4	0
Decanal	0.3	0
1,8-Cineole	0	0.7 -9.0

Minor components

Coumarins and psoralens (bergaptens) cause phototoxic problems. These are not found in distilled oils, or FCF oils. There are many Methoxy-flavones which are indicators of authenticity of Orange oil but demand sophisticated detection techniques. α- and β-sinensals contribute to the orange aroma together with other components e.g. (+) – valencene and (–) – caryophyllene (45).

Both Orange oils have GRAS status.

Adulteration

Cold-pressed Orange oil has a limonene content of about 95%, but the 10-fold oil has 80 % and the 25-fold oil only 57%. In fact, limonene can decrease to 0.2% on total deterpenation: this raises other components to very high levels e.g. linalool becomes 28% and decanal 17%. This indicates that there is a wide range of possible Orange Oils produced. Numerous ways of adulterating Orange Oils persist; mixing with Citrus oil terpenes, distilled Bitter Orange and other Citrus oils or addition of synthetic limonene to Sweet Orange oil is frequent, Terpeneless, sesquiterpeneless and concentrated Bitter and Sweet Orange oils are blended in as well as distilled Orange oil etc. Antioxidants like BHT and BHA are frequently added to prevent oxidation and increase the shelf life. Sweet Orange oil is often used as a substitute for Bergamot oil. (See also Lemon oil).

Toxicity

LD$_{50}$ - Bitter Orange >5g/kg (oral) rat; >10g/kg (dermal) rabbit.
Sweet Orange >5g/kg (oral)rat; >5g/kg (dermal) rabbit.
Irritation/Sensitisation – Nil at 8% bitter, 10% Sweet Orange oil. 1/200 dermatitis patients were sensitive to Sweet Orange and 3/200 to Bitter Orange (50). Cutaneous irritation has been reported to Bitter Orange oil and there was a case of severe dermatitis involving fingers, hands, forearms and face of a girl peeling the fruit (18).
Phototoxicity – High to low phototoxicity especially if used undiluted on the skin.

Bioactivity

Pharmacology – Orange oil was spasmogenic on guinea-pig ileum *in vitro* (32).There was an increase in tone and rhythmic contractions as well as peristalsis in the dog *in vivo* (47).
Antibacterial action – Was very variable: Orange oil affected 4/25 bacteria (15), 4/5 bacteria (59), 19/25 bacteria and 10/20 Listeria monocytogenes varieties (32), however in another study there was no effect on 5/5 Listeria (6). Bitter Orange Oil vapour was effective against 1/5 bacteria (42).
Antifungal action – was generally low 3/5 fungi were affected by both Sweet and Bitter Orange Oil (38) and 2/3 fungi were affected at low concentration by Florida Orange oil (32). Sweet Orange oil was effective against 14/15 fungi (41).
Miscellaneous action – There was no antioxidant effect by Florida Orange oil (32). An antidepressant effect was produced by spraying Orange oil at patients (49).

Uses

Dried orange peel is included in most pharmacopoeias. Citrus aurantium was the most commonly used plant by Puerto Ricans. The maladies for which it was used included sleep disorders, gastro-intestinal disorders, respiratory ailments and raised blood pressure (37).

PALMAROSA~   *Graminae*

Cymbopogon martini Stapf.
syn.Andropogon martini Roxb. var. motia

Known as East Indian or Turkish Geranium oil.

Extraction: Steam distillation of partly dried grass.
Origin: India, Madagascar, Central America, Brazil.

Main components, %

Geraniol	76-83
Geranyl acetate	5-11.8
Linalool	2.3-3.9
Neral	0.3-0.6
Farnesol	0.3-1.5
β-Caryophyllene	1-1.8

Palmarosa has GRAS status.

Adulteration

Gingergrass is a common adulterant as it grows wild, but has a lower geraniol content; turpentine, citronella and synthetic geraniol are often added. Palmarosa itself is often used as a substitute for Geranium and Rose oil.

Toxicity

LD_{50} – >5g/kg (oral) rat and >5g/kg (dermal) rabbit.
Irritation/Sensitisation – Nil at 8% (human).
Phototoxicity – Nil reported.

Bioactivity

Pharmacology – There was a spasmolytic effect on guinea-pig ileum *in vitro* (32).
Antibacterial action – Was shown against 23/25 bacteria and 18/20 Listeria monocytogenes varieties (32). The vapour affected 1/5 bacteria (42).
Antifungal action – Moderate activity was shown against 3/3 fungi (32).
Miscellaneous action – There was moderate antioxidant action found (32). CNV data shows that it is a relaxant oil (56,57).

PATCHOULI~ *Labiatiae*

Pogostemon cablin (Blanco) Benth.
syn. P.patchouly Pellet, var. suavis Hook.f.

Extraction: Steam distilled dried leaves of the tree.
Origin: Indonesia, India.

Main components, %

Patchouli alcohol	31-46
α-Guaiene	10-15
Caryophyllene	2-4
α-Bulnescene	13-17
Seychellene	6-9.4
α-Patchouline	3.9-5.9
β-Patchouline	1.7-4.8
Pogostol	0-2.7

An iron-free Patchouli oil is also produced which has a lighter odour. Minor components, trace components like (+) – norpatchoulenol of under 0.5% and nortetrapatchoulol at 0.001% contribute greatly to the aroma (45).

Patchouli has GRAS status.

Adulteration

Cedarwood, Clove oil sesquiterpenes and Cedarwood derivatives are frequently used for cutting the oil, also methyl abietate, hydroabietic alcohols, vetiver residues, camphor residues, Gurjun Balsam oil (detected by α-Gurjunene),Copaiba Balsam oil, Castor oil and isobornyl acetate etc.

Toxicity

LD_{50} – >5g/kg (oral) rat; >5g/kg (dermal) rabbit.
Irritation/Sensitisation – Nil at 20% (human). This should be reduced to 0.1% in people with dermatoses.
Phototoxicity – Nil reported.

Bioactivity

Pharmacology – There was a strong spasmolytic action on guinea-pig ileum *in vitro* (32).
Antibacterial action – Was variable: 6/25 different bacteria were affected but 15/20 Listeria monocytogenes varieties (32). The vapour affected 2/5 bacteria (42).

Antifungal action – Was very low against 3 fungi (32) and 2/15 fungi (41). *Miscellaneous action* – No antioxidant activity was found (32). The spraying of Patchouli-based mixtures proved to be an anti-depressant to patients (49). There was an increase in mice motility on application of Patchouli vapour (12).

Uses

There is a long tradition of using Patchouli on Indian carpets and rugs to prevent insect colonisation.

PETITGRAIN~ *Rutaceae*

Citrus aurantium L. subsp. amara
syn. Bigarade
Citrus limonum (L.) Burm.f.

Extraction: Steam distilled leaves and twigs of bigarade lemon and often other citrus tree
Origin: France, Italy, Algeria, Tunisia, Morocco, Spain & Paraquay.

Main components, %

Linalool	19-27
Linalyl acetate	46-55
Neryl acetate	2-3
α-Terpineol	4-8
Geraniol	2-4
Myrcene	1-6

Note: There is a wide variation in the odour and composition of Petitgrain oils derived from different species.

Minor components

There are over 400 known components many of which contribute to the odour e.g. β-Damascenone, β-Ionone, 2-Isopropyl-3-methoxypyrazine and α-Terpinyl acetate (45).

Petitgrain oil has GRAS status.

Adulteration

Lemongrass is frequently used to adulterate or substitute for Petitgrain, also synthetic citral, lemon oil, Leptospermum citratum etc. The Paraguayan Petitgrain is very harsh and it has to be deterpenated first; it can then form the base for Neroli oil substitute. Petitgrain itself is used to adulterate or substitute for the very expensive Neroli, which is extracted from the flowers of these citrus trees.

Toxicity

LD_{50} – For both Bigarade and Lemon Petitgrain:
>5g/kg (oral) rat, >5g/kg (dermal) rabbit.
Irritation and Sensitisation – Nil at 7% for Bigarade and 10% Lemon. Sensitisation is rare even in sensitive individuals: 1/200 dermatitis patients were affected (50).
Phototoxicity – Nil.

Note: The oil is not expressed from the rind, and therefore does not contain furocoumarins. However, adulteration with expressed citrus oils could cause phototoxicity.

Bioactivity

Pharmacology – There was an initial spasmogenic action followed by a spasmolytic action on guinea-pig ileum *in vitro* (32).

Antibacterial action – Was very strong: 5/5 bacteria were affected by the oil (38) and 1/5 by the vapour (42) and 21/25 bacteria and 16/20 Listeria monocytogenes varieties were affected (32). However, in another study no activity against 5/5 Listeria was found (6).

Antifungal action – Was generally good: 5/5 fungi were affected (38); 5/5 different fungi were affected and there was a moderate effect on 3/3 fungi (32). Low to moderate action was found against 15/15 fungi (41).

Miscellaneous action – Petitgrain had a small antioxidant action (32).

PINE~ *Pinaceae*

Pinus sylvestris L.
Scotch Pine

Extraction: Steam distillation of the Pine needles.
Origin: Siberia, C. and S. Europe.

Main components, %

α-Pinene
β-Pinene
Limonene } Variable
Borneol
Bornyl Acetate
γ-Carene

Pine oil has GRAS status.

Adulteration

Mixtures of camphene, pinenes and isobornyl acetate etc are used.

Toxicity

LD_{50} – >5g/kg (oral) rat; >5g/kg (dermal) rabbit.
Irritation/Sensitisation – Nil at 20% (human).
Phototoxicity – Nil.

Bioactivity

Pharmacology – Nil reported
Antibacterial action – 4/5 bacteria were affected, but a combination of other essential oils with Pine oil resulted in decreased activity of those oils (18). There was no effect on the Tubercle bacilli but given in conjunction with subeffective doses of dihydrostreptomycin, Pine oil (10mg as a 2% solution in Olive oil injected intramuscularly once a week) had a therapeutic effect on experimental tuberculosis in guinea-pigs (18).
Antifungal effect – Moderate action against 15/15 fungi was found (41) and weakly inhibited 2/12 phytopathogenic fungi (39) and 2/5 fungi (38).

ROSE~ *Roseaceae*

Bulgarian Rose oil; Rose Otto; Turkish Rose oil
Rosa damascena Mill.

French Rose oil; Moroccan Rose oil
Rosa centifolia L.

Other roses:
Rosa gallica L.
Rosa alba L.

Extraction: Steam distillation of freshly picked flowers; solvent extraction giving the concrete followed by alcohol extraction to give the Absolute.
Origin: Bulgaria, Morocco, Turkey, France, Italy.

Main components, %

	Rose oil	Absolute
Citronellol	18-55	18-22
Geraniol	12-40	10-15
Nerol	3-9	3-9
Phenylethyl alcohol	1-3	60-65
Stearopten	0	8-22

Minor components

Rose oxide	0.1-0.5
β-Damascone	0.01
β-Damascenone	0.14
β-Ionone	trace − 0.03

Note: There are at least 300 components in Rose oil of which β-Damascenone at only 0.14 % in the oil gives the true rose-like odour due to its perceptibility at very low concentrations which gives it 70% of the total odour compared to Citronellol which provides only 4.3% of the odour (45).

All three main Rose oils have GRAS status.

Adulteration

As this is one of the most expensive oils on the market, adulteration is very sophisticated and difficult to detect. However, numerous synthetic components can be used to boost the diluted true oil e.g. phenylethyl alcohol, diethylphthalate, citronellol, geraniol, isoeugenol, heliotropine, cyclamal, amyl salicylate and fractions from geranium oil such as rhodinol etc. The Absolute is often adulterated also by synthetic Palmarosa fractions, Peru Balsam oil, Costus oil, Clove bud absolute etc. Rose Otto is often a combination of the original distillate plus the redistilled water (cohobation water) which apparently contributes most of the phenyl ethyl alcohol.

Toxicity

LD_{50} – Rose oil Bulgarian, Moroccan and Turkish i.e. Rosa Damascena and R.centifolia: – >5g/kg (oral) rat; 2.5g/kg (dermal) rabbit.
Rose Absolute (French) – >5g/kg (oral) rat; uncertain for dermal.
Irritation/Sensitisation – Nil at 2% (human).
Phototoxicity – Nil reported.

Bioactivity

Pharmacology – A spasmolytic action on guinea-pig ileum *in vitro* was produced by Rose oils and absolutes (32).
Antibacterial action – 1/5 bacteria were affected by Rose kazanlik vapour (42).
Antifungal action – Nil reported
Miscellaneous action – Rose oil had no effect on mice activity (13) and had either no effect on CNV (25) or a stimulating one (36,57).

ROSEMARY~ *Labiatiae*
Rosmarinus officinalis L.

Extraction: Steam distilled leaves, or entire plant without woody parts.
Origin: Spain, France, Italy, Russia, Middle East.

Main components, %

1,8-Cineole	50 (7-60)
Myrcene	7 (0-10)
α-Pinene	11 (3-24)
β-Pinene	1 1-8)
p-Cymene	2 (0-3)
Camphor	10 (3-21)
Borneol	1-2
Bornyl acetate	2-3

Rosemary has GRAS status.

Adulteration

Addition of cineole and various terpenes, Cypress oil, Camphor, Eucalyptus (globulus, radiata), turpentine fractions, fractions from synthetic terpineol production, light Cedarwood fractions and Spanish Sage etc. Flower oil from low-grade Spanish Rosemary is often deterpenized to give a good quality oil.

Toxicity

LD_{50} – >5g/kg (oral) rat;>5g/kg (dermal) rabbit.
Irritation/Sensitisation – Nil at 10% (human).
Phototoxicity – Not tested.

Bioactivity

Pharmacology – Rosemary oil was markedly spasmogenic but had some spasmolytic effect also on guinea-pig ileum *in vitro* (32). There was a relaxant effect on the tracheal smooth muscle of rabbit and guinea-pig *in vitro* (3).
Antibacterial action – Was very potent 5/5 bacteria were affected (38), 21/25 bacteria (15) and 21/25 with 16/20 Listeria monocytogenes varieties affected (32). However in another study there was no effect on 5/5 Listeria varieties (6). Rosemary oil vapour and acetylated Rosemary vapour were effective against 1/5 bacteria (42).
Antifungal action – Was variable 5/5 fungi were affected (38), and very poor action was found against 3/3 fungi (32). Low to moderate action was found against 15/15 fungi (41).

Miscellaneous action – No antioxidant action was detected (32).
Rosemary had a stimulating effect on the mouse (10) and CNV studies also showed this stimulating action in man (25).

Note: Rosemary has been implicated in inducing epilepsy in people with family trends and there was an increase in the incidence of epileptic fits in epileptic patients massaged with Rosemary oil (9). Tonico-clonic convulsions were produced in animals by Rosemary *in vivo* and an inhibition of $Na+$ and $K+$ gradients *in vitro* (53).

Uses

Rosemary is carminative and mildly irritant (37). It has been used in hair lotions and liniments.

ROSEWOOD~   *Lauraceae*

Bois de Rose
Aniba roseadora var.amazonica Ducke
syn.A.parviflora Mez.
syn. Ocotea caudata Mez.

Extraction: Steam distillation of comminuted wood.
Origin: Brazil, Peru, Guyana.

Main components, %

Linalool	85.3-94
1,8-Cineole	0-1.6
Limonene	0.6
cis-Linalool Oxide	0-1.5
Trans-Linalool Oxide	0-1.3
Terpinen-4-ol	0.4
α-Terpineol	3.5

Adulteration

Ho Wood leaves and branchlets are now used more often instead of Rosewood for obvious ecological reasons. Synthetic Linalool and Linalyl acetate are probably used even more often.

Toxicity

LD_{50} – >5g/kg (oral) rat; >5g/kg (dermal) rabbit.
Irritation/Sensitisation – Acetylated – Nil at 12%.
Phototoxicity – Nil reported.

Bioactivity

Pharmacology – A spasmolytic action was found on guinea-pig ileum *in vitro* (32).
Antibacterial action – Was very potent against 24/25 bacteria but only 12/20 Listeria monocytogenes varieties (32).
Antifungal action – Was moderate against 3/3 fungi (32) and from poor to good action against 5/5 fungi (41).
Miscellaneous action – No antioxidant action was found (32).

SAGE~ *Labiatiae*

Dalmatian Sage – Salvia officinalis L.
syn. English, True, Garden or Red Sage
Spanish Sage – Salvia lavandulaefolia Vahl.
also: Greek Sage – S.triloba L.

Extraction: Steam distillation of partly dried leaves
Origin: England/Spain

Main components ,%

	Dalmatian	Spanish
1,8-Cineole	8-24	18-54
α-Thujone	15-48	0
β-Thujone	2-25	0
Camphor	2-27	1-36
Linalool	0-32	0-9
α-Pinene	trace	4-20
β-Pinene	trace	6-19
Camphene	trace	4-30
p-Cymene	trace	1-5

Note: these two sages not only differ in composition with each other but also with Clary Sage (p).

Both Dalmatian and Spanish oils have GRAS status.

Adulteration

Dalmatian Sage is often adulterated with Salvia triloba which has a cineole content of 42-64%. Thujone is obtained from American Cedarwood and added to the Dalmatian Sage or Greek Sage. Palmarosa oil is also added.

Toxicity

LD_{50} –
Dalmatian 2.6g/kg (oral)rat; >5g/kg (dermal) rabbit.
Spanish >5g/kg (oral) rat; >5g/kg (dermal) rabbit.
Greek not tested.
Irritation/Sensitisation – Both nil at 8% (human)
Phototoxicity – Nil for Spanish oil; Dalmatian not tested.

Note: Thujone is regarded as toxic. However, the Flavourings and Food Regulations 1992 give the following amounts of Thujone to be used in foods:
α-, β- thujone permitted at 0.5mg/kg food

Bitters have permitted values of 35mg/kg
Sage-based foods – 25mg/kg
High-alcohol drinks – 10mg/kg

Bioactivity

Pharmacology – The two sages (Dalmatian and Spanish) had a spasmolytic effect on guinea-pig ileum *in vitro* (32).

Antibacterial action – Was very low for Dalmatian Sage: 3/25 bacteria were affected (15), 16/25 bacteria and 6/20 Listeria monocytogenes varieties were affected (32) and in another study, no activity was found against 5/5 Listeria (6). Spanish Sage oil inhibited the growth of only 1/10 bacteria (18). Dalmatian Sage vapour affected 2/5 bacteria (42)

Antifungal action – Both Dalmatian and Spanish Sage had an effect on 5/5 fungi (41). There was almost a negligible effect on 3/3 filamentous fungi (32). Grecian Sage affected 14/15 fungi and Spanish Sage 15/15 fungi (41).

Miscellaneous action – There was an antioxidant effect by Dalmatian Sage (32). "Sage" was found to have no effect on CNV (25,36). "Sage" in large doses caused convulsions in rats and humans (44).

Uses

Sage oil has carminative properties (37).

SANDALWOOD~ *Santalaceae*

Santalum album L.

(East Indian and Indonesian oils)

Note: The famous Mysore oil is now not available commercially.
West Indian Sandalwood is from Amyris balsifera L. (Amyris oil).
Australian Sandalwood is from Fusanus spicatus (Eucarya spicata), but no longer available due to past exploitation.

Extraction: Steam distillation of powdered dried wood of the semiparasitic tree.
Origin: India, Carribean.

Main Components, %

α-Santalol	45–60
β-Santalol	17–30
epi-β-Santalol	4.3
trans-β-Santalol	1.6
α-Santalene β-Santalene	} 10
epi-β-Santalene	6
cis-Lanceol	1.2

Sandalwood has GRAS status.

Adulteration

Amyris oil, Araucaria, Cedarwood oil, Castor oil and Copaiba oil are often added. Odourless organic solvents may also be used as diluents e.g. liquid paraffin, glyceryl acetate, diethylphthalate (DEP), benzyl benzoate, benzyl alcohol and dipropylglycol (DPG). There are also synthetic substitutes eg. Sandela and Sandalore which are much cheaper.

Toxicity

LD_{50} – >5.0g/kg (oral) rat; >5g/kg (dermal) rabbit.
Irritation/Sensitisation – Nil at 10% (human).
Phototoxicity – Nil reported.

Bioactivity

Pharmacology – Sandalwood oil produced a spasmolytic effect on guinea-pig ileum *in vitro* (32).
Antibacterial action – 1/5 bacteria were affected by Sandalwood vapour (42).
Antifungal action - There was very low activity against 3/15 fungi (41).

Miscellaneous action – The German medicine "Salvarsan" contains Sandalwood oil. Sandalwood is a relaxant according to CNV data (25).

Uses

Formerly used as a urinary antiseptic at a dose of 0.3-1ml (37).

TEA TREE~ *Myrtaceae*

Melaleuca alternifolia (Maiden & Betche) Cheel
also:M.linariifolia, M.dissiflora and many other species.

Extraction: Steam distilled leaves and branchlets of trees.
Origin: Australia

Main components, %

α-Pinene	2.2
α-Terpinene	7.5
1,8-Cineole	5.6 (not to exceed 15)★
γ-Terpinene	17.5
p-Cymene	3.0
Terpinen-4-ol	45.0 (not to be less than 30)★
α-Terpineol	2.7
Terpinolene	3.1

The components vary tremendously due to the different varieties of Melaleuca trees and the propensity of chemotypes; trees grown next each other have been found to have a different oil composition (58).

★Australian Standard for Melaleuca, terpinen-4-ol type oil.

Tea tree oil is granted temporary acceptability for use in foods.

Adulteration

Because of the Standards imposed, a great deal of blending occurs using oils from various cultivars and species. Terpinen-4-ol may also be added together with other terpenes.

Toxicity

LD_{50} – 1.9g/kg (oral) rat; >5g/kg (dermal) rabbit.
Irritation/Sensitisation – Nil at 1% (human).
1,8-Cineole is a known sensitiser, and therefore, the content of cineole is reduced by the Australian Standards (58).
Phototoxicity – Nil reported.

Bioactivity

Pharmacology – There was an initial spasmogenic action followed by a spasmolytic action on guinea-pig ileum *in vitro* (32).
Antibacterial action – Depended to some extent on the composition of the oil. 1,8-cineole has low antibacterial activity whilst terpinen-4-ol has high activity and p-cymene is even higher. Therefore, although the latter

is at only 2.5% on average in Tea tree oil, it exerts a large influence (58). Antibacterial studies have shown small effects (5) and excellent effects against 24/25 bacteria and 20/20 Listeria monocytogenes varieties (32). The vapour affected 1/5 bacteria (42)

Antifungal action – Was substantial 5/5 fungi were affected (38) and Tea tree oil was very active against 3/3 fungi (32) and 8 fungi including Candida albicans, P.ovale (dandruff) and Trichophyton (Tinea) (5,44). *Miscellaneous action* – There was no antioxidant effect (32).

Uses

A study of Tea tree oil against benzoyl peroxide at 5% on 124 patients suffering from dermatitis showed that Tea tree had a slower but ameliorating effect with fewer side-effects (7). Other clinical studies have included use as an antiseptic in dentistry, numerous skin conditions including acne, furunculosis (boils), vaginal thrush, foot problems, coughs and colds (43).

THYME~   *Labiatiae*

Thymus vulgaris L.
Thymus zygis L.

Red Thyme, syn.Spanish Thyme
White Thyme
Sweet Thyme

Extraction: Steam distillation of partially dried plant.
Origin: Spain, France, Italy, Turkey, E.Europe, USA.

Main components, %

	Red thyme	*Sweet Thyme*
Thymol	45-48	0
Carvacrol	2.5-3.5	0.7
Geraniol	0	30.4
Geranyl acetate	0	50.1
β-Caryophyllene	1.3-7.8	4.1
α-Pinene	0.5-5.7	0
p-Cymene	18.5-21.4	0
1,8-Cineole	3.6-15.3	0
Terpinolene	1.8-5.6	0

Note: The data given above is from typical commercial samples. However, there are numerous publications on the composition of different Thyme samples from different cultivars and different countries.

There is great confusion over the nomenclature and taxonomy of the Thyme, Origanum and Marjoram group. There are hundreds of varieties and cultivars, and also numerous chemotypes of Thyme which result in a wide range of different compositions. The main commercial Thyme oils are the Red or White (thymol and carvacrol chemotype) and the Sweet thyme (geraniol-rich chemotype). The White Thyme should be a rectified Red Thyme containing over 60% of Thymol, but in practice it is often an Origanum oil containing over 60% carvacrol.

Red Thyme oil has GRAS status.

Adulteration

Origanum and various Spanish essential oils are used instead of true Thyme oil or as diluents. White Thyme is often a compounded oil containing pine oil fractions, terpineol, Rosemary, Eucalyptus and Red Thyme fractions, and/or p-cymene, pinene, limonene, caryophyllene and Origanum.

Toxicity

LD_{50} – Red Thyme oil; 4.7g/kg (oral) rat, >5g/kg (dermal) rabbit.
Irritation/Sensitisation – Red Thyme oil – nil at 8%; however when applied to animal skin undiluted it proved severely irritating..
Phototoxicity – Nil.

Bioactivity

Pharmacology – Both Red and Sweet Thyme oils were spasmolytic when applied to guinea-pig ileum *in vitro* (32).
Antibacterial action – Differred for Sweet and Red Thyme oils. Red Thyme was extremely active on 25/25 bacteria, whilst Sweet Thyme was active on only 14/25. Red Thyme was also active against 20/20 Listeria monocytogenes varieties, whilst Sweet Thyme was active against 14/25 (32). An unidentified Thyme oil was active against 22/25 bacteria (15). Both Red and White Thyme vapours were very active against 5/5 bacteria (42).
Antifungal action – There was a similar moderately good action against 5/5 fungi by both Red and White Thyme oils (59). There were some differences between samples of Red Thyme oils as well as White oil on 3/3 fungi(32). Red Thyme was very active against 18/18 fungi including Trichophyton mentagrophytes (41).
Miscellaneous action – There was variable but good antioxidant action by both Red and Sweet Thyme oils (32). Thyme is stimulating according to CNV data (57).

Uses

Thyme oil has been used in mouth washes, gargles, cough linctuses and a special Thyme Elixir for treating whooping cough and bronchitis (0.05-0.3ml of Thyme oil BPC). External applications as a rubefacient and counter-irritant include dilution with olive or other oils (37).

VETIVER~   *Graminae*
syn. Vetivert
Vetiveria Zizanoides Stapf.

Extraction: steam distillation of washed and sun-dried rootlets and rhizomes of grass.
Origin: Java, East Africa, Central America, Indonesia, Phillipines, India.

There is a wide variation in the odour and chemical composition of oils from different origins.

Main components, %
Vetiverol	10
Vetiverone	9
Vetiverone esters	variable

Vetiver oil is approved by the FDA for food use.

Adulteration

Often adulteration is at the distillation stage as other grass roots can be mixed together e.g. Cyperus. The oil can also be "cut-back" with fractions from the isolation of Vetiverol. Cutting can then be made with Caryophyllene, Cedarwood derivatives, Amyris oil etc.

Toxicity

LD_{50} – >5g/kg (oral)rat; >5g/kg (dermal) rabbit.
Irritation/Sensitisation – Nil at 8% (human).
Phototoxicity – Nil.

Bioactivity

Pharmacology – A weak spasmolytic effect was found on guinea-pig ileum *in vitro* (32).
Antibacterial action – The vapour was active against 1/5 bacteria (42)
Antifungal action – There was low activity against only 2/15 fungi (41).

YLANG YLANG~   *Anonaceae*
Cananga odorata Hook f. et Thomson

Extraction: Steam distillation of fresh, early morning-picked flowers of the tree.
Origin: Reunion, Comores, Phillipines and Indonesia.

Main components, %

Germacrene D	5 -10
Linalool	2 -19
p-Cresyl Methyl Ether	0.5 -16.5
Benzyl Acetate	3 -25
Benzyl Benzoate	2 -10
Geranyl Acetate	3 -10
β-Caryophyllene	1 -1

Ylang Ylang oil has GRAS status.

Note: The Extra grade has more benzyl acetate and p-cresyl methyl ether, a high proportion of linalool and a low proportion of sesquiterpenes compared to the other grades, but these are very variable and it is impossible to correlate the grades among suppliers. The flowers are distilled for varying times and the fractions are completely different in composition. There is a gradation in the quality of the oil based on the time of distillation. The most expensive is fraction 1 of least duration i.e. 3 hours (Extra Superior), and there is a diminution of cost with the later fractions, an extra hour (Extra), a further hour (Grade 1), a further 0.6 hours (Grade 2) and, lastly, 16 hours (Grade 3) which makes the total time of distillation 22 hours. The later Grades are often substituted by Cananga oil.

Adulteration

Cananga oil is often used as a substitute or adulterant. Gurjun Balsam oil is also used, but can be detected by the α-gurjunene content. The Extra Grades are frequently mixed with the other lower grades. Adulteration also occurs with vanillin, p-cresyl methyl ether, methyl benzoate, geraniol, isoeugenol, isosafrole, benzyl alcohol, benzyl benzoate, benzyl propionate and cinnamate, anisyl acetate, anisyl alcohol, Copaiba oil, Peru Balsam and other pure oils and synthetic components.

Toxicity

LD_{50} – >5g/kg (oral)rat; >5g/kg (dermal) rabbit.
Irritation/Sensitisation – Nil at 10% (human), however 4/200 patients with dermatitis showed a sensitisation reaction at 2% (50). Note: Cananga oil,

unlike Ylang Ylang, is irritating to the skin of rabbit when applied undiluted.

Phototoxicity – Nil.

Bioactivity

Pharmacology – There was a spasmolytic effect on guinea-pig ileum *in vitro* by fractions 1, 2, and 3 of the oils (32).

Antibacterial action – The vapour affected only 1/5 bacteria (42).

Antifungal action – There was low to moderate activity against 5/5 fungi (38) for an unspecified Ylang Ylang oil. There was a low, mainly fungistatic effect, against 11/15 fungi (41).

Miscellaneous action – Ylang Ylang was a stimulant when applied using soaked cotton wool in masks or by spraying at patients (49). It was also shown to be a stimulant according to CNV data (36,57).

8 | Bibliography

1 Achterrath-Tuckermann, U., Kunde, R., Flaskamp, E., Issac, O. and Thiemer, K (1980). Planta medica 39.38-50.
2 Albert-Puleo, M. (1980).1. Ethnopharmacol. 2 337-344.
3 Aquel, M.B. (1991). J. Ethnopharmacol 33, 57-62.
4 Arctander, S. (1960). Perfume and Flavour Materials of natural Origin. Elizabeth: New Jersey, USA.
5 Asre, S. (1994). Chemical Composition and Anti-microbial Activity of some Essential Oils. M.Sc. Thesis. Macquarie University, Sydney, Australia.
6 Aureli, P., Cosnstantini, A. and Zolea, S. (1992). J. Food Protection. 55. (5). 344-348.
7 Bassett, I.B., Panovitz, D.L., Barnetson, R. St.C. (1990). Med. J. Austr. 153, 455-488.
8 Bennett, A., Stamford, I.F., Tavares, I.A., Jacobs, S., Capasso, F., Mascolo, N. Antore, G., Romano, V. and Di Carlo, G. (1988). Phytotherap. Res. 2 124-130.
9 Betts, T. (1994). Aromatherapy Quarterly. (Spring) 19-22.
10 Buchbauer, G., Jirovetz, L., Jager, W., Dietrich, H., Plank, C.. and Karamat, E. (1991). Zeltschr Naturforsch 46, 1067-1072.
11 Buchbauer, G. (1992). Perfumer and Flavourist 18, 19-24.
12 Buchbauer, G., Jager, W., Jirovetz, L., Ilmeberger, J. and Dietrich, H. (1993a). In: Bioactive Volatile Compounds from Plants. Ed. Teranishi et al. ACS Symposium Series 525.
13 Buchbauer, G., Jirovetz, L., Czejka, M., Nasel, C. and Dietrich, H. (1993b). 24th International Symposium on Essential Oils, Berlin.
14 Culpepper, N. (1835). The Complete Herbal. Th. Kelly, London.
15 Deans, S.G. and Ritchie, G. (1987). Int.J. Food Microbiol. 5, 165-180.
16 Dew, M.J. (1984). Br J. Clin. Pract. 38, 394-398.
17 Fenaroli's Handbook of Flavour Ingredients, (1979). 2nd Edition. CRC Press. Vol.1
18 Food and Cosmetic Toxicology: Monographs on Essential Oils produced by RIFM (1973-1982). continued as Food and Chemical Toxicology (1982-1992).
19 Gattefosse, RM., Aromatherapy (1993). C.W. Daniel & Co. Ltd. Saffron Walden, Translated from French 1937
20 Haginiwa, J., Harada, M. and Morishita, 1. (1963). Yakugaku Zasshi 83, 624.
21 Herrman, E.C. and Kucera, L.S. (1967).124ii 869-74.
22 Imaseki, I. and Kitabateke, Y. (1962). Yakaguku Sasshi 82. 1326-1328.
23 Janssens, J., Laekeman, G.M., Pieters, A.C., Totte, J. Herman, A.G. and Vlietinck, A.J. (1990). J. Ethnopharmacol. 29 179-188.
24 Korbely, I. and Florian, E. (1971 ii). Gyogyszereszet 15. 462
25 Kubota, M., Ikemoto, T., Komaki, R. and Iniu, M. (1992). Paper: 12th Int. Congress on Flavours, Fragrances and Essential Oils. Vienna, Austria.
26 Lawrence, B. (1975-94). Monographs on Essential Oils: Perfumer and Flavourist.
27 Le Guérer, A. (1993). Scent. The Mysterious and Essential. Powers of Smell. London: Chatto and Windus.
28 Lewis, W.H. and Elvin-Lewis, M.P.F. (1977). Medical Botany. John Wiley and Son: New York, London, Sydney. p.408-410.
29 Lis-Balchin, M., Simmonds, M., Hart, S. and Deans, S. (1992). Paper: 12th International Congress on Flavours, Fragrances and Essential Oils, Vienna, Austria.
30 Lis-Balchin, M., and Hart, S. (1994a). Herbs, Spices and Medicinal Plants: In Press.

31 Lis–Balchin, M., Deans, S. and Hart, S. (1994b). Poster: 25th International Symposium on Essential Oils, Grasse, France.

32 Lis–Balchin, M., Deans, S. and Hart, S. (1994c). Paper: 25th International Svmposium on Essential Oils, Grasse, France.

33 Lis–Balchin, M., Simmonds, M., Hart, S., and Deans, S.G. (1994d). Herbs, Spices and Medicinal Plants: In Press.

34 Lis–Balchin, M., Deans, S. and Hart, S. (1995a) . J. Essent. Oil.Res. Submitted Oct. 1994.

35 Macht, D.I. and ChingTing, G. (1921). J. Pharmacol Exp. Therap. 18 (5) 361-372.

36 Manley, C.H. (1993). Critical Rev. in Food Science and Nutrition. 39 (1). 57-62.

37 Martindale.(1972). The Extra Pharmacopoeia. The Pharmaceutical Press. 26th Edition.

38 Maruzzella, J. C., (1960) Soap Parfum Cosmet. 33, 835-7.

39 Maruzzella, J.C. and Balte, J. (1959). P. Dis. Reptr 43. 1143.

40 Maruzzella, J.C. and Henry, P.A. (1958). J. Am. Pharm Ass. 47. 294.

41 Maruzzella, J.C. and Liguori, L. (1958). J. Am. Pharm Ass. 47. 250.

42 Maruzzella, J.C. and Sicurella, N.A. (1960). J. Am. Pharm. Ass. 49, 692.

43 Mayo, W.L. (1992). Int. J. Alternative and Complementary Medo. Dec. 13-16.

44 Millett, Y., Jouglard, J., Steinmetz, M., Tognetti, P., Joanny, P. and Arditti, J. (1981). Clin. Toxicol. 18, (12) 1485-1498.

45 Ohloff, G. (1944). Scent and Fragrances. Springer-Verlag.

46 Pages, N., Fournier, G., Luyer, F. le, Marques, M-C. (1990). Plant Med. Phytotherapie. 24 21-26.

47 Plant, O.H. and Miller, G.H., (1926). J. Pharmocol. exp. Therap. 27, 149.

48 Rees, W.D., (1979). Br. Med. J. 2, 835-836.

49 Rovesti, P. and Colombo, E. (1973). Soap, Perfumery and Cosmetics. 46, 475-7.

50 Rudzki, E. Grzywa, Z., and Bruo, S. (1976). Contact Dermatitis 2, 196-200.

51 Shafran, I., Maurer, W. and Thomas, F.B., (1977). New Engl. J. Med 296. 694.

52 Stamford, I.F., Bennett, A., Greenhalf, J. (1978). Vet. Record 103. 14-15.

53 Steinmetz, M.D., Vial, M. and Millet, Y. (1987). J. Toxicol. Clin. Exp. 7, (4) 259-271.

54 Stoddart, D.M. (1994). The Scented Ape: The Biology and Culture of Human Odour. Cambridge University Press.

55 Toller, S. and Dodd, G.H., (1988). Perfumery: The Psychology and Biology of Fragrance. Chapman & Hall.

56 Toller, S. and Dodd, G.H., (1992). Fragrance: The Psychology and Biology of Perfume. Elsevier Applied Science, London and New York.

57 Torii, S., Fakuda H., Kanemoto, H., Miyanchi, R., Hamanzu, Y. and Kavasaki. (1988). In Perfumery p. 107-20.

58 Williams, L.R. (1992). 12th Int. Congress Flavours, Fragrances and Essential Oils, Vienna, Austria Oct 4-8.

59 Yousef, R.T. and Tawil, G.G. (1980). Pharmazie 35, 698-701.

Abbreviations

BMA Butylated hydroxytoluene
BMT Butylated hydroxyariline
CNV Cognitive Negative Variation
CTFA Cosmetic, Toiletary and Fragrance Association.
FDA Food and Drug Administration, USA.
FEMA Flavour and Extract Manufacturers' Association.
GC Gas Chromatography
GRAS Generally Recognised as Safe
IFRA International Fragrance Association
ISO International Organisation for Standardization
NIOSH National Institute of Occupational Safety and Health, USA.
RIFM Research Institute of Fragrance Materials, USA

OTHER BOOKS FROM AMBERWOOD PUBLISHING ARE:

Aromatherapy – A Guide for Home Use by Christine Westwood. All you need to know about essential oils and using them. £1.99.

Aromatherapy – For Stress Management by Christine Westwood. Covering the use of essential oils for everyday stress-related problems. £2.99.

Aromatherapy – For Healthy Legs and Feet by Christine Westwood. A comprehensive guide to the use of essential oils for the treatment of legs and feet, including illustrated massage instructions. £2.99.

Plant Medicine – A Guide for Home Use by Charlotte Mitchell MNIMH. A guide to home use giving an insight into the wonderful healing qualities of plants. £2.99.

Woman Medicine – Vitex Agnus Castus by Simon Mills MA, FNIMH. The wonderful story of the herb that has been used for centuries in the treatment of women's problems. £2.99.

Ancient Medicine – Ginkgo Biloba by Dr Desmond Corrigan BSc(Pharms), MA, Phd, FLS, FPSI. Improved memory, circulation and concentration are associated in this book with medicine from this fascinating tree. £2.99.

Indian Medicine – The Immune System by Desmond Corrigan BSc(Pharms), MA, Phd, FLS, FPSI. An intriguing account of the history and science of the plant called Echinacea and its power to influence the immune system. £2.99.

Herbal First Aid by Andrew Chevallier BA, MNIMH. A beautifully clear reference book of natural remedies and general first aid in the home. £2.99.

Natural Taste – Herbal Teas, A Guide for Home Use by Andrew Chevallier BA, MNIMH. A beautifully illustrated book containing a comprehensive compendium of Herbal Teas giving information on how to make it, its benefits, history and folklore. £2.99.

Signs & Symptoms of Vitamin Deficiency by Dr Leonard Mervyn BSc, PhD, C.Chem, FRCS. A home guide for self diagnosis which explains and assesses Vitamin Therapy for the prevention of a wide variety of diseases and illnesses. £2.99.

Causes & Prevention of Vitamin Deficiency by Dr Leonard Mervyn BSc, PhD, C.Chem, FRCS. A home guide to the Vitamin content of foods and the depletion caused by cooking, storage and processing. It includes advice for those whose needs are increased due to lifestyle, illness etc. £2.99.

Eyecare Eyewear – For Better Vision by Mark Rossi Bsc, MBCO. A complete guide to eyecare and eyewear including an assessment of the types of spectacles and contact lenses available and the latest corrective surgical procedures. £3.99.